W9-AJZ-949

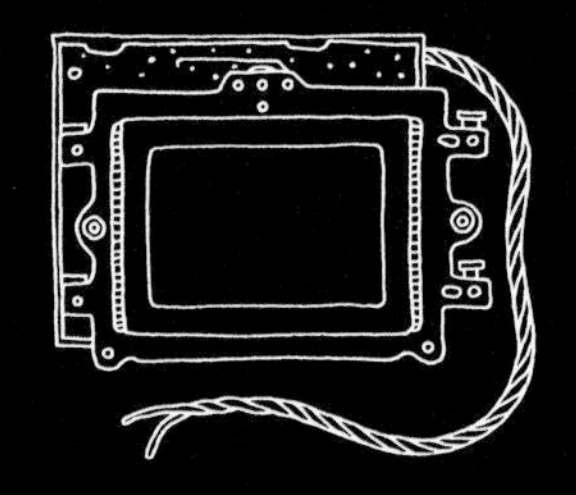

ACTIVE PIXEL SENSOR

Seeing the world through a smartphone

Think of the last picture you took: Chances are it was taken—and then sent—on a smartphone.

In 2002, Nokia and Sanyo first strapped a nascent technology called an active pixel sensor to their cellular phones. Since then, the way humans record and share experiences has fundamentally changed. An active pixel sensor is a grid of tiny transistors, covered by various filters to discern different colors of light that are then translated into images. The media we share those images through have become some of the fastest growing companies in the world: Instagram and Snapchat, born of an era fascinated with sharing images, are worth billions of dollars, and Facebook is betting its empire that we want to share live video with friends wherever we go. These businesses' impact on the future will be predicated on this technology.

In a market dictated by likes and social influence, the intimacy of recording a unique perspective from a personal device has also produced a new generation of celebrities: YouTubers and social-media stars, who have the freedom to capture and share video and photos from wherever they go.

The active pixel sensor has also more recently changed the way machines operate by giving them the gift of vision. Factory robots once relegated to pre-programmed movements can now handle a wider variety of tasks, and robots being built by startups like Starship could autonomously navigate our constantly changing human world. Coupled with algorithms that can outperform even humans at tasks such as facial recognition, machines with active pixel sensors pave the way for a world in which robots move among us, if not as equals, then certainly as partners.

↑ Active pixel sensor on display. (Mathery)

THE INVENTION THAT TURNED OUR PHONES INTO CAMERAS WAS DEVELOPED BY NASA FOR SPACE TRAVEL

Next time you take a selfie, thank Eric Fossum, a professor of engineering at Dartmouth College. Smartphone cameras, webcams, backup cameras in cars, and even some medical-imaging machines wouldn't be possible without his 1992 invention, the active pixel sensor. Fossum's sensor was smaller and far more power-efficient than the competition, which enabled machines to see their surroundings like never before.

"It was developed under NASA funding in the jet propulsion laboratory in Pasadena, California. We were trying to miniaturize cameras for interplanetary space travel. When we were done, we said, 'Wow, not only is this useful for space, but this is pretty useful for here on this planet.'

"Smartphones were not on the radar initially at all. We were thinking about web cameras and we made the first ones from swallowable pill cameras that swim through your intestines and take pictures along the way. And then there were two other niche applications.

↑ (Courtesy of CNN Türk)

"One of the first early ones was automotive. We worked with a company called Gentex in Michigan, and they were looking at how to put features into cars, automatic-dimming headlights, and how to build brake sensors automatically.

"Another thing that was also big at the time was dental X-ray sensors. A small company in New York came to us and said, 'Hey, we think this would be good for dental radiography.' So we collaborated in that work as well, and that's become pretty ubiquitous in dental offices; nobody uses film anymore.

"At some point, there seemed to be interest in putting cameras with phones. It started as a detachable accessory you clip on to your phone. Later they were integrated into the phone.

"This is not politically correct, but it's a true story. We were approached for this camera phone by a company that thought that Japanese teenage girls would want to share their shopping experience with other Japanese teenage girls. Having it built into the camera would be really convenient for that. It was really the initial application for this technology: I think it was just to take a picture of shoes or jewelry or a dress and to share it."

FaceTiming a coup

Journalist Hande Firat was having dinner on July 15, 2016 when she heard that the military was trying to overthrow Turkish president Recep Tayyip Erdoğan. She rushed to the Ankara studio of CNN Türk and began negotiating an interview with the president. Erdoğan's team asked to talk to her through Periscope or Skype, but Firat only had FaceTime installed on her smartphone.

Just after midnight, Erdoğan's face appeared live on Turkish television—shaky, saturated, low-res. Firat positioned a microphone in front of her phone and Erdoğan began to speak. "Go to the streets and give them their answer," the president said. "I am coming to a square in Ankara." The people answered Erdoğan's call, and the coup eventually failed.

It was the first time a sitting president avoided regime change via FaceTime. For months, Firat refused repeated offers from Turkey and Middle Eastern countries for a historical artifact: her iPhone 6S.

ROBOTS WITH EYES ARE CHANGING THE WAY FARMERS DO THEIR JOBS

Electronic eyes are changing the way we farm. Modern agricultural practices are beginning to use active pixel sensors to increase productivity and help feed the world's rapidly growing population. Instead of driving a tractor in distinct patterns through his fields, a farmer can now let autonomous systems take over so he can focus on seeding. Self-driving sprayers that coat plants with liquid nutrients or pesticides can navigate tight rows for him, while grain harvesters can judge the quality and quantity of a farmer's yield.

Since John Deere's first tractor with autonomous steering capabilities was introduced in 2001, the company says more than 200,000 of these machines are now being used in countries such as the US, China, Russia, and Brazil. An October 2016 US Department of Agriculture survey found that 80% of large farms in the US use GPS-guided autonomous farm equipment.

The companies building these machines, such as John Deere and CNH Global, have been striving to produce more autonomous systems for nearly a decade and have changed the way farmers think about their land. On a large farm, there could be millions of individual plants growing, which means it has traditionally been easier for farmers to focus on what a whole field needs to be more productive rather than on individual organisms. But an autonomous sprayer could dole out nutrients on a plant-by-plant basis or flag problematic plants that could affect the yield of others. "For a field of corn in Iowa, you might plant 32,000 seeds per acre (79,000 per hectare), and you can recognize those individual plants," says Lane Arthur, a technologist at John Deere. "We see a future with more and more imaging as a part of it."

Farmers can also use drones equipped with cameras to gauge how many of their seeds have germinated—handy information when deciding how best to nurture nascent plants. Through these technologies, farming suddenly becomes more precise by magnitudes.

Drones and autonomous vehicles can help with specific tasks, but they can't replace the versatility of a farmhand. Arthur believes it will be a long time before we have a fully automated farm, but he thinks camera-borne automation will multiply the farmers' effectiveness. "I don't think about it in terms of taking jobs away," he says. "There's a lot of work that needs to happen, and we're going to need some machines to do it."

Jobs for machines with eyes

If you blinked, you missed it—the robot uprising has already begun. Humans are being replaced by robot employees who never need a break and don't require dental insurance. White collar, blue collar, or no collar at all, these are some of the professions that could be filled by machine labor:

Factory assembly worker
Retail worker
Cashier
Bank teller
Security guard
Shepherd
Fruit picker
Delivery driver
Long-haul truck driver
Soldier
Surgeon
Radiologist
Housekeeper
Pharmacist

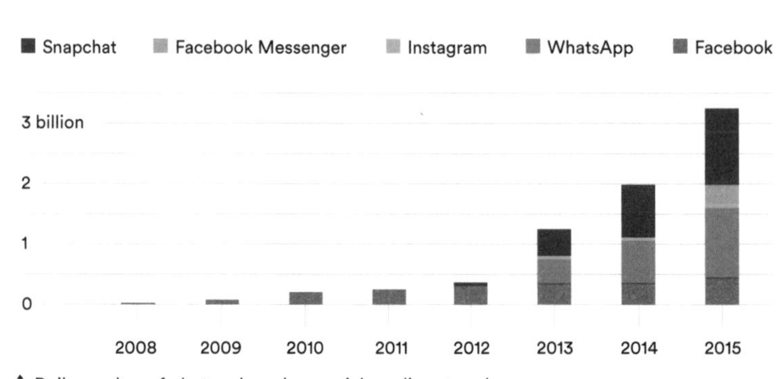

↑ Daily number of photos shared on social-media networks.
Data: Kleiner Perkins Caufield & Byers

A DRONE'S EYE VIEW: CAPE TOWN'S APARTHEID REMAINS

From an aerial view, Cape Town's scenic beauty gives way to a stark reminder of the country's past and its continued racial segregation. Pictured above are the neighborhoods of Hout Bay and Imizamo Yethu, which show the stark differences in development. "The actual city infrastructure has been created to keep various groups of people separate from one another. You can see this in all urban centers in South Africa, but Cape Town is particularly pronounced," says Johnny Miller, a photographer who has been living in Cape Town since 2012. Under apartheid, South African cities and towns were designed to give white people access to the central business districts and homes in the leafy suburbs. Black people had to live far outside of the city, only venturing in for work. While apartheid has been over for more than two decades, integrating these living spaces has remained a challenge, and socioeconomic inequality is still stubbornly divided by race. (April 9, 2016, Johnny Miller)

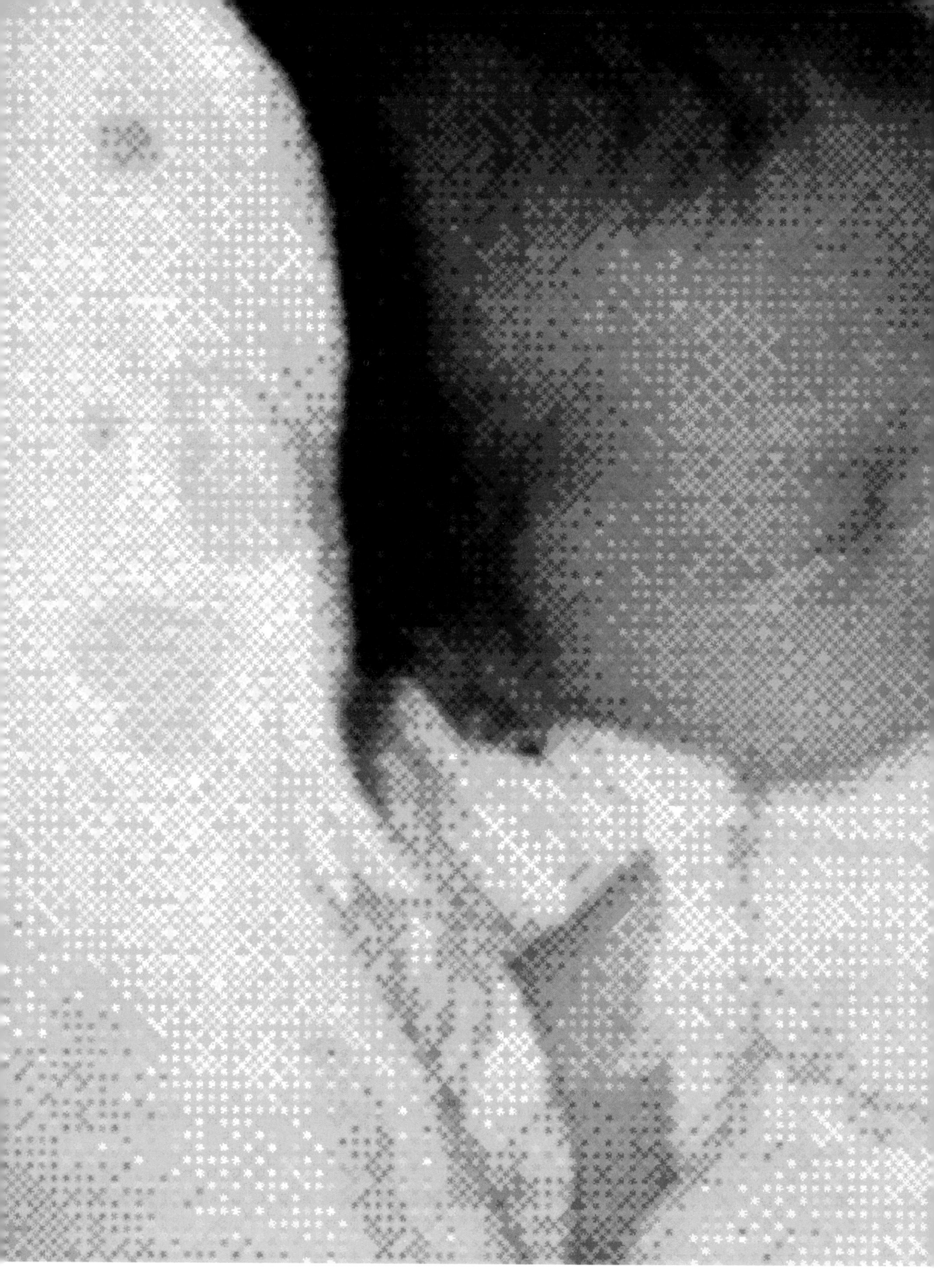

Philippe Kahn, a French software engineer and entrepreneur in northern California, jerry-rigged the first cellphone camera capable of taking and sending photos in real time. Using his digital camera, flip phone, and laptop, he made history on June 11, 1997 when his daughter Sophie was born: An image of the pink, swaddled baby, which he sent to

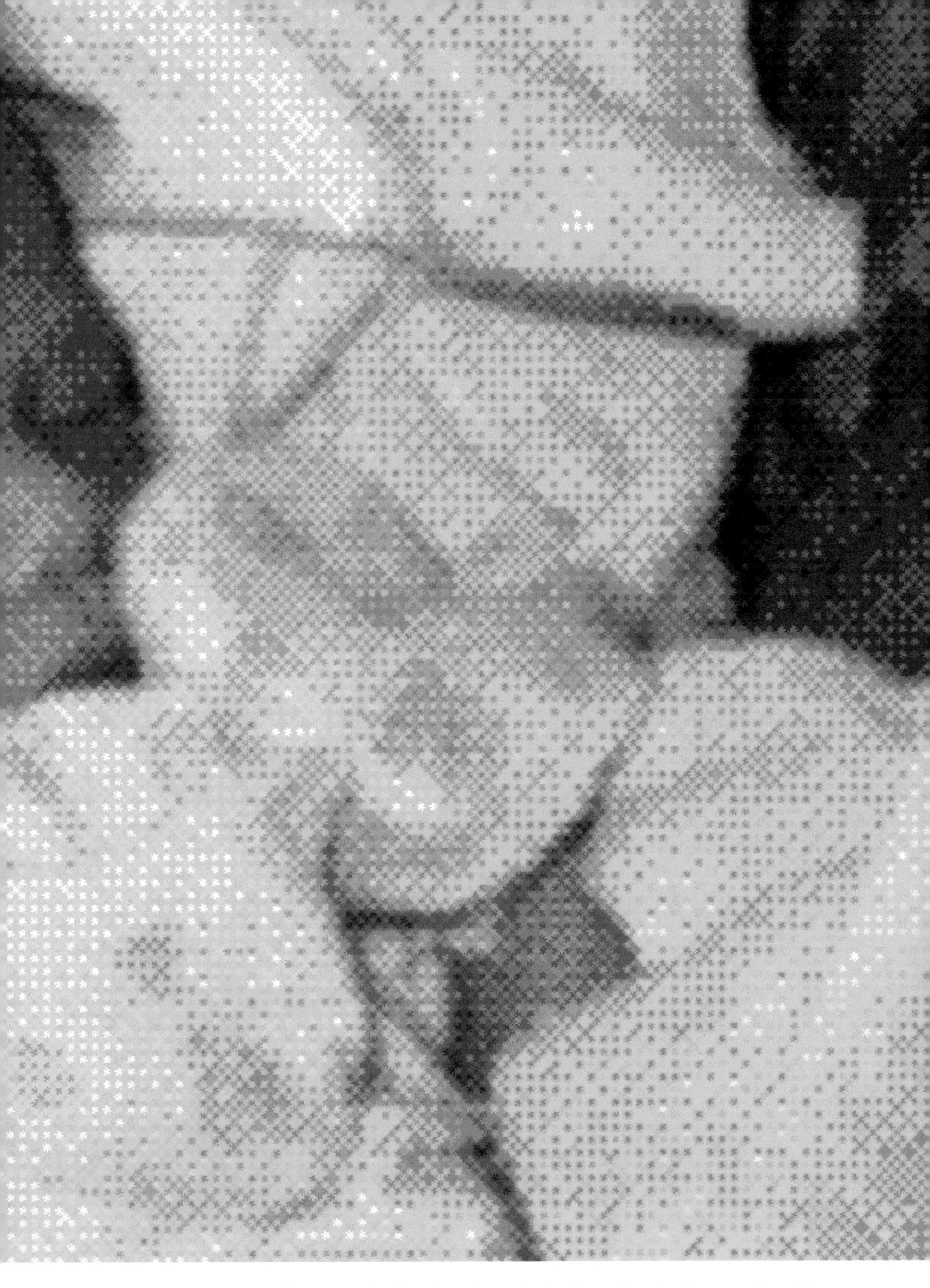

over 2,000 people, became the first photo taken by a phone instantly shared over the web. Three years later, Sharp began selling the first integrated cameraphones in Japan. (Courtesy of Philippe Kahn)

FRONT-FACING CAMERAS WERE NEVER INTENDED FOR SELFIES

Rose-colored filters

When Instagram was in development, the app's co-founder, Kevin Systrom, took some invaluable advice from then-girlfriend Nicole Schuetz. She told him that she wouldn't be posting images to his app because her photos weren't terrific, compared to those of a friend. "But that friend used filter apps to enhance his photos," Systrom pointed out. Schuetz's suggestion? "Ah, that's it, add filters," Systrom told National Public Radio in 2016. "We just need to be able to make people feel like their photos are worthy of sharing." (Nicole is now Nicole Systrom; the two were married in 2016.)

When Instagram launched in 2010, it included 11 filters. By the beginning of 2017, it had 40 filter options. Today, filters are used on about 57% of all images posted to Instagram, though not on most selfies. According to a 2016 analysis by graphic-design-program maker Canva, Skyline is the filter most likely to attract "likes" to food photos, Valencia is the most popular choice for landscapes, and Kelvin's warm look is most appreciated on fashion shots. The same study found that Slumber, which softens images, is the most "liked" for selfies.

In 2003, Sony introduced a squat flip phone that would have been forgotten if not for its 0.3 megapixel camera that could be turned to face the caller. The Ericsson Z1010 was the first mobile device with a front-facing camera. Little did designers know that this simple feature, intended to enhance business meetings, would usher in the age of selfies.

Social-media platforms and photo-sharing apps like Instagram would make the selfie the lingua franca of millennials. It was the perfect format for the mobile, DIY-minded, and social-media-savvy generation. By turning the camera on themselves, users became the models, photographers, art directors, image retouchers, and publishers of their images. The casual self-portrait format—at times aided by a long, retractable stick—became so ingrained in daily life that Oxford Dictionaries named "selfie" the 2013 word of the year.

The numbers vary, but they're all too big to ignore. Google estimated in 2014 that over 93 million selfies are taken every day on Android devices, and in her book *Je Selfie Donc Je Suis (I Selfie Therefore I Am)*, psychoanalyst Elsa Godart estimates that young adults will take a staggering 25,700 selfies in their lifetime.[01] Before the selfie mode was invented, people were more sparing with their self-portraits.

But front-facing cameras were never intended for vanity. Sony's mobile-phone designers thought the camera-flip feature would be used for video-conference meetings so that users would no longer have to be tethered to a desktop or laptop to convene Skype calls.

When Steve Jobs unveiled the iPhone 4 in 2010, he demonstrated the new front-facing camera's intended use by making the first public FaceTime call to Jony Ive, Apple's chief design officer. "I grew up here in the US with *The Jetsons* and *Star Trek* and communicators, and just dreaming about this—dreaming about video calling—and it's real now," Jobs gushed.

The wifi slowed down during that historic call, straining their casual banter. During the awkward lag, Ive, grinning in front of a modern-art painting, essentially modeled how great the iPhone camera would be for snapping selfies.

By 2015, Apple formally acknowledged how often users turned their high-definition cameras toward themselves by introducing a dedicated folder for selfies in Photos. For the first time, selfie lovers' vanity was quantified and tagged. But the world was not ready for such an honest mirror. Among the most googled queries for iOS 9 was, "How do I delete the selfie folder?"

[01]
Selfies can be a dangerous game. Between March 2014 and September 2016, 76 people in India died in selfie-related accidents. Mumbai demarcated 16 no-selfie zones in 2016, many of them along the city's seafront. Violations carry a 1,200 rupee ($18) fine.

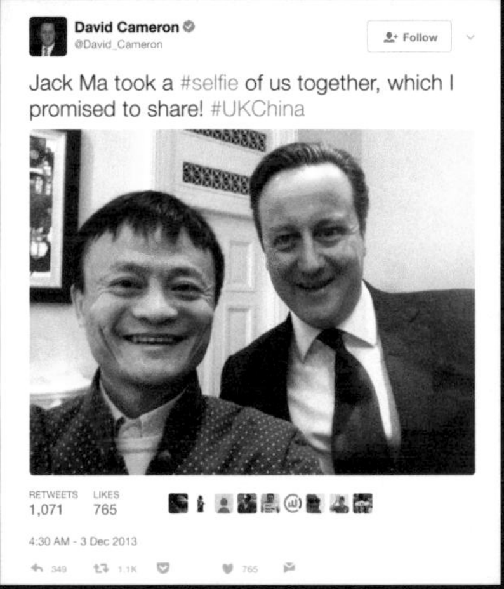

↑ During an official trip to China, then-British prime minister David Cameron shared a selfie with Alibaba founder Jack Ma. Cameron later appointed Ma to his business-advisory group in 2015. (Twitter, Dec. 3, 2013)

↑ Then-US vice president Joe Biden's first selfie was with then-president Barack Obama on a trip to Oakdale, Pennsylvania. (Instagram, April 16, 2014)

↑ German chancellor Angela Merkel in a selfie with Brazilian football star Marta after the 2014 FIFA World Cup in Brazil. (Instagram, July 22, 2014)

Narendra Modi
@narendramodi
Follow
It's selfie time! Thanks Premier Li.
RETWEETS 5,686
LIKES 8,114
6:22 AM - 15 May 2015

↑ Chinese premier Li Keqiang and Indian prime minister Narendra Modi in front of the Temple of Heaven in Beijing. (Twitter, May 15, 2015)

↑ Then-US presidential candidate Donald Trump poses behind a taco bowl at Trump Tower in New York. (Twitter, May 5, 2016)

Geert Wilders
@geertwilderspvv
Follow
Together with @MLP_officiel
RETWEETS 113
LIKES 177
7:08 AM - 29 Jan 2016

↑ Dutch Party for Freedom leader Geert Wilders and Marine Le Pen, then-leader of France's National Front party, take a selfie at a far-right convention in Milan. (Twitter, Jan. 29, 2016)

THIS POMERANIAN NAMED JIFF IS PURSUING A CAREER IN HOLLYWOOD

↑ 237,608 likes

↑ 251,811 likes

↑ 264,017 likes

↑ 299,254 likes

Meet Jiff, a Pomeranian lovingly known by millions of strangers as Jiffpom. With over 5 million followers, this adorable dog is the most followed animal on Instagram. He was born in Illinois but moved to Hollywood in 2013 to pursue a career beyond the incredibly small screen. Jiff, whose website describes him as an "extremely talented movie actor/model," has appeared in TV shows, movies, commercials, and music videos, like the 2014 music video for Katy Perry's Grammy-nominated hit "Dark Horse." Perry said he was "basically the star of the show, stealing all of my thunder." Jiff has a full-time manager and is represented by United Talent Agency. Managers are reluctant to discuss specific figures, but a general rule of thumb is that a social-media star—human or otherwise—can command $2,000 and up per gig after breaking the 100,000-follower mark. Jiff is expertly leveraging his following to build an empire: He sells branded calendars, phone cases, emoji stickers; has his own licensing business, complete with a Jiffpom style guide; and has a live-action TV series and cartoon movie both currently in development. (Courtesy of @jiffpom/Instagram)

MAERSK

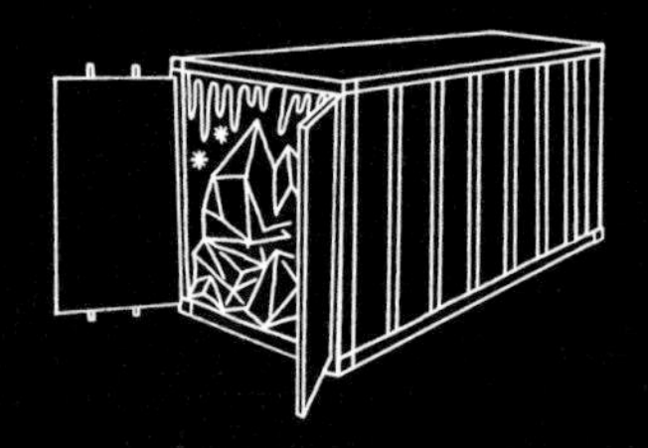

REEFER

Keeping the supply chain fresh

Refrigeration received a cool reception when it was introduced in the US in the late 1800s. Shoppers thought warehouse owners were stockpiling fruit to control prices and feared that cold storage ruined flavor. They got over that pretty quickly. By the mid-20th century, refrigerated transportation had overhauled the Western middle-class diet, granting year-round access to an abundance of proteins and produce from far-flung places.

It's now commonplace to breakfast on bananas from Ecuador, bacon from the Netherlands, and coffee beans harvested in Vietnam—and pay very little for the pleasure. That's made possible by the unglamorous, metal-sided shipping containers invented in the 1950s that still move nearly 90% of the world's trade. Thanks to the refrigerated "reefer" container, fresh meat, fruit, and vegetables can be had for cheap, everywhere in the world, and at any time of year.

In the cold-chain logistics market, total revenue is growing at 16% per year, and as middle classes expand in developing economies, demand for reefer-transported products is rising. This desire is led by Asia, and especially China: The cold chain already delivers two thirds of China's frozen french fries from the US and a similar share of ice cream from France. In turn, refrigerated drugs like insulin are also making their way to China via reefers.

To capitalize on this demand, shipping businesses are accelerating, revamping operations, and updating their trusty reefers. New "smart" containers have begun to provide near-real-time data on their locations so that companies are never in the dark about where their goods are, and can maintain finely tuned temperatures to ensure everything from flowers to medicines arrives in peak condition. Meanwhile, smarter warehouses and sci-fi-like autonomous delivery vehicles are expanding distribution networks' reach and speed, all aimed at erasing any evidence that breakfast traveled halfway around the world before landing on your plate.

↑ Refrigerated shipping container with peas. (Mathery)

NEARLY 90% OF WORLD TRADE MOVES BY SHIPPING CONTAINER

By some accounts, the shipping container has played a bigger role in hastening globalization than all the international trade agreements signed over the past 50 years.

By standardizing the dimensions of the boxes that house the world's cargo, shipping containers have drastically reduced loading and unloading times at the world's ports. Before 1965, dock laborers moved an average of 1.7 metric tons of cargo per hour. Almost immediately following the container's introduction, they were able to move 30. Today, containerized shipping supplies the world with sneakers, flat-screen TVs, and cheap avocados, supporting essential export businesses in developing countries.

Since the container's arrival, however, the marine shipping business has failed to innovate. Most shipping companies still rely on humans to manually enter location data, for instance, partially because the network connections that gave rise to the Internet of Things on land are not strong enough across the high seas. The industry average for on-time delivery is also only about 64%, according to research firm Drewry. Often, damaged or late-arriving cargo forces both shipper and receiver to pay for costly, last-minute workarounds.

A few companies are now finally adopting "smart" technology. Maersk, by far the industry's largest player, has outfitted its cold-storage shipping containers with tracking devices that measure location, temperature, and air quality. In 2017, French firm Traxens intends to add 130,000 smart devices to the vessels of two of the industry's other major players. Each device, essentially a small transmitter, uses radio technology to report a container's location to customers, as well as possible break-ins, dangerous temperature changes, and sudden jolts. And Rolls-Royce has been designing a fully autonomous, remote-controlled drone ship, a prototype of which it plans to test by the end of the decade.

Progress is slow, but the payoff could be huge: Nearly 90% of world trade moves by shipping container, according to the International Chamber of Shipping. Each small improvement in the efficiency of this vast industry saves lots of time and money on both ends of the supply chain and opens up new opportunities for trade—just as the container itself did half a century ago.

↑ Drawing from 1958 US patent for the twistlock by K.W. Tantlinger.

The twistlock

A shipping container's corner castings, made of perforated steel, are what allow a "twistlock" to be inserted, which securely binds each container to the ship's deck or to the containers stacked above and below. Together, the castings and twistlocks allow over 95% of the world's containers to be lifted, stacked, and carried over rails, roads, and oceans.

Designing a connector that would work anywhere in the world was not easy. In the mid 20th century, shipping lines, trucking companies, and railway operators all competed to have their models adopted as the standard. According to Marc Levinson's history of containerization, *The Box*, it took a radical act to break the deadlock: In January 1963, US shipping magnate Malcom MacLean directed his company, Sea-Land, to release its patent rights to the design of its containers' corner castings. Giving away the design reduced MacLean's potential gain in the near term but allowed the bickering parties to converge on a single model, resulting in a far richer ultimate prize: an efficient, uniform, international system.

The royalty-free use of Sea-Land's fitting became the basis of a global standard; today's corner castings and twistlocks are direct descendants of the design McLean gave away.

The port of Singapore sits at the mouth of the Strait of Malacca, a gateway to Asia once favored by ancient Roman, Greek, Chinese, and Indian traders. Built in 1819, it began accepting container ships in 1972. It is now the world's second-busiest port after Shanghai's, and often credited with Singapore's economic rise. The strait remains a critical shipping route for oil sent east from the Gulf states and other trade; the Economist estimates that 40% of world maritime traffic passes through here every year. In the 1980s, Singapore issued a series of banknotes highlighting the importance of marine trade in its history. (Satellite view of the port of Singapore on June 6, 2017. Photos courtesy of BanknoteBook.com and Planet Labs)

FOR THE SAKE OF FRESH FOOD, BARBARA PRATT TRAVELED THE WORLD IN A SHIPPING CONTAINER

[02] In the 1930s, the New York City restaurant Schrafft's was so proud of its imported, out-of-season ingredients that menus listed miles traveled: The fruit cocktail's components had racked up a combined 8,000 miles (12,900 km), and the veggie salad clocked 22,000 miles.

Barbara Pratt was hired in 1977 by shipping company Sea-Land (now Maersk) to study refrigeration. She traveled the world inside a shipping container turned laboratory. Today, Pratt directs refrigerated technical services for Maersk North America.

"The laboratory we built had three different compartments: It had what we called an engine room where we had a diesel-fuel tank, a diesel generator for power, a water tank, and a hot-water heater. We had a laboratory section in the middle that had your typical equipment but also had things like a gas chromatograph, a computer, a fume hood, and a microscope—those types of things. And then we had an office section that had bunk beds, a couple of desks and cabinets, a microwave, and a refrigerator.

"Over the following years we worked on various different commodities—almost any commodity that moves today: We worked on pineapples, watermelons, tomatoes, peppers, bananas, all kinds of perishables, trying to see if we could extend the shelf life of those products and carry them, say, for two weeks' transit instead of one.

"Part of the reason we had to stay in the container was the unknown reliability of the computers that we were working with at the time. With the state of the industry and the microprocessors that exist today, it's possible to monitor what's happening remotely. I used to have to stay with the containers to monitor what was going on inside them when they were only 20 or 30 feet from me.

"In the future, I think there's going to be a continued focus on quality, on wanting to know if there was a problem with something, being able to react faster, and being able to know what to do. For example, if you were planning on moving into a market and holding the product there for four months, if you know that there's a problem with your product, maybe you move it into the market faster and sell it in the first month instead of four months later.

"When it comes to the consumer, maybe they're okay with only eating grapes for six months of the year, but I think the consumer over the last 20 years has gotten used to going to the grocery store and getting more than pickles, tomatoes, and dried meat. They're used to fruits and vegetables—they *want* fruits and vegetables—and their economies are such that they can afford the fruits and vegetables." [02]

↑ Barbara Pratt, director of refrigerated services for Maersk, working in a laboratory built in a shipping container. (Circa 1978, courtesy of Maersk)

The size of the circles above indicates the volume of the 10 fresh fruits that were shipped the most worldwide in 2015. The blue area indicates the temperature required to keep each fruit from spoiling en route. Bananas were the most shipped item, with 16.9 million metric tons, or approximately 141 billion individual pieces of fruit. The banana has been part of the global cold chain since 1902, and its ideal shipping temperature—13°C-14°C (55°F-57°F)—has become one of six standard reefer settings, referred to simply as "banana." (Data: Zim Integrated Shipping Services, Drewry Maritime Research)

UNILEVER KNOWS PRECISELY WHEN AND WHERE YOUR ICE CREAM MELTED

Shipping for all

Ask entrepreneurs who have worked with shipping companies to import or export goods, and they'll tell you stories of Kafkaesque frustrations and bureaucracy. A startup that wants to take advantage of cheap ocean freight will [03] usually interact with a complex network of middlemen to find quotes, book shipments, file the appropriate customs paperwork, and track the movement of their goods from port to port.

To help out businesses on a budget, Alibaba launched a service for its customers in early 2017 to book space in a Maersk shipping container. It joins several other would-be "Ubers" of shipping, like Palo Alto-based Shipwire, which provides on-demand warehousing and order-fulfillment functions, and Israel's Freightos, which allows businesses to book air-, ocean-, or truck-freight deliveries online. This nascent shift toward on-demand shipping services could soon make it easier for anyone with a small batch of products to take advantage of global supply chains cheaply and efficiently.

Since 2015, consumer-goods giant Unilever has required the installation of tracking devices on all trucks carrying its products. Managers can monitor the location of every shipment leaving a Unilever facility and get alerts if anything is off about the temperature-sensitive shipments. They can see if ice cream has been through extreme temperature changes and can even verify that it hasn't traveled above optimal altitudes—which is important, because certain formulas for ice cream expand at high altitudes, splitting packaging or cracking candy shells.

Year after year, surveys show shoppers around the world want faster and more reliable deliveries—and at lower prices. In a poll of American consumers, consulting firm AlixPartners found that shoppers expect to wait an average of 4.8 days for delivery, down from 5.5 days in 2012. The share of people willing to wait more than five days for a product they bought fell from 74% to 60% over the same period. In the UK, retailers are doing a roaring trade with "click and collect," in which shoppers pick up online purchases in store.

As a result, companies like Walmart and Amazon are now demanding more transparency, flexibility, and speed from their suppliers. They want to make smaller orders more frequently instead of holding too much inventory themselves, which is costly. They also want to be able to cancel or change those orders as demand fluctuates.

For suppliers like Unilever and Procter & Gamble, this doesn't come cheap. In order to make changes, they must closely monitor the locations and conditions of every shipment in near-real time.

But as quickly as companies speed up their supply chains, consumer behavior changes even faster. To cope, some delivery companies like Deutsche Post DHL are experimenting with driverless vehicles. Some trucking companies offer to deliver *and* assemble furniture for their clients' customers. The need for speed has also led Chinese manufacturers like Hisense, one of the world's largest TV makers, to set up factories in Mexico and eastern Europe so that it can build and ship its products to key markets in days instead of weeks.

[03]
How much cheaper is marine shipping compared to air freight? Shipping 10,000 copies of this book from printers in Bologna, Italy to New York would cost $1.28 per copy and take about several weeks. By air, it would cost $5.15 per copy and arrive in 48 hours.

↑ A drone carrying medical supplies takes off from Zipline headquarters in Rwanda. (Oct. 2016. Photo by Stephanie Aglietti/AFP/Getty)

AIRSHIPS, DELIVERY DRONES, AND FLYING CARS: THE FUTURE OF SHIPPING

Amazon plans to roll out delivery drones in 2017, but they won't fly solo for long. In 2016, the company filed a patent application for drone collectives: interlinked swarms that would be able to fly for long periods, with individual drones breaking off for deliveries.

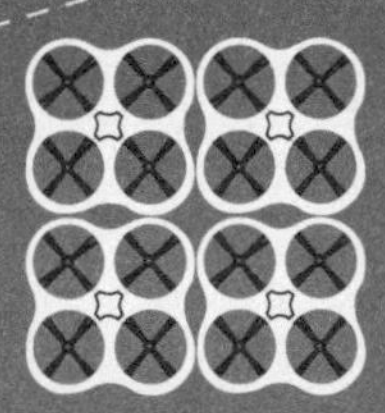

Lockheed Martin's helium-filled hybrid airships are as long as an NFL football field and can move 20 metric tons of cargo. Able to land almost anywhere, seven ships have already been ordered by a Canadian mining company. Lockheed says they'll be flying by 2019.

Dubai-based port operator DP World and US startup Hyperloop One are looking at applying still-nascent Hyperloop travel technology at marine terminals in Dubai and Los Angeles. Levitating pods shot through pressurized tubes would speed up port-to-inland depot delivery and ease road traffic.

In Rwanda, drones are already transporting blood supplies to doctors in rural areas. Made by the US-based startup Zipline, the medical delivery drones are launched by catapult and drop their cargo with a mini parachute.

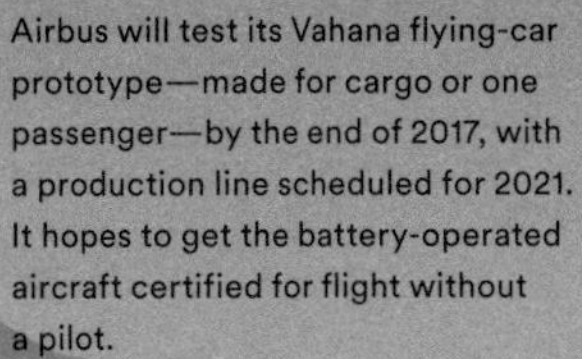

Mercedes Benz, Volvo, Daimler, and other auto brands are test-driving autonomous trucks, while Tesla and Ford promise driverless trucks in five years. Such fleets could save the US $170 billion annually in labor and fuel—but could also put 1.7 million American drivers out of work.

Airbus will test its Vahana flying-car prototype—made for cargo or one passenger—by the end of 2017, with a production line scheduled for 2021. It hopes to get the battery-operated aircraft certified for flight without a pilot.

To keep delivery trucks from clogging US streets and highways, Amazon proposes a subterranean delivery system. According to its 2016 patent filing, boxes will move underground through conveyor belts and vacuum tubes.

In 2013, Rolls-Royce began designing a crewless, remote-controlled container ship, and it plans to test WWa prototype by 2020. The ship's captain would stay in an onshore control deck, dispatching drones to the vessel for repairs and observations as it crosses the ocean.

FROM KENYA TO JAPAN: HOW THE WORLD'S FLOWERS TRAVEL

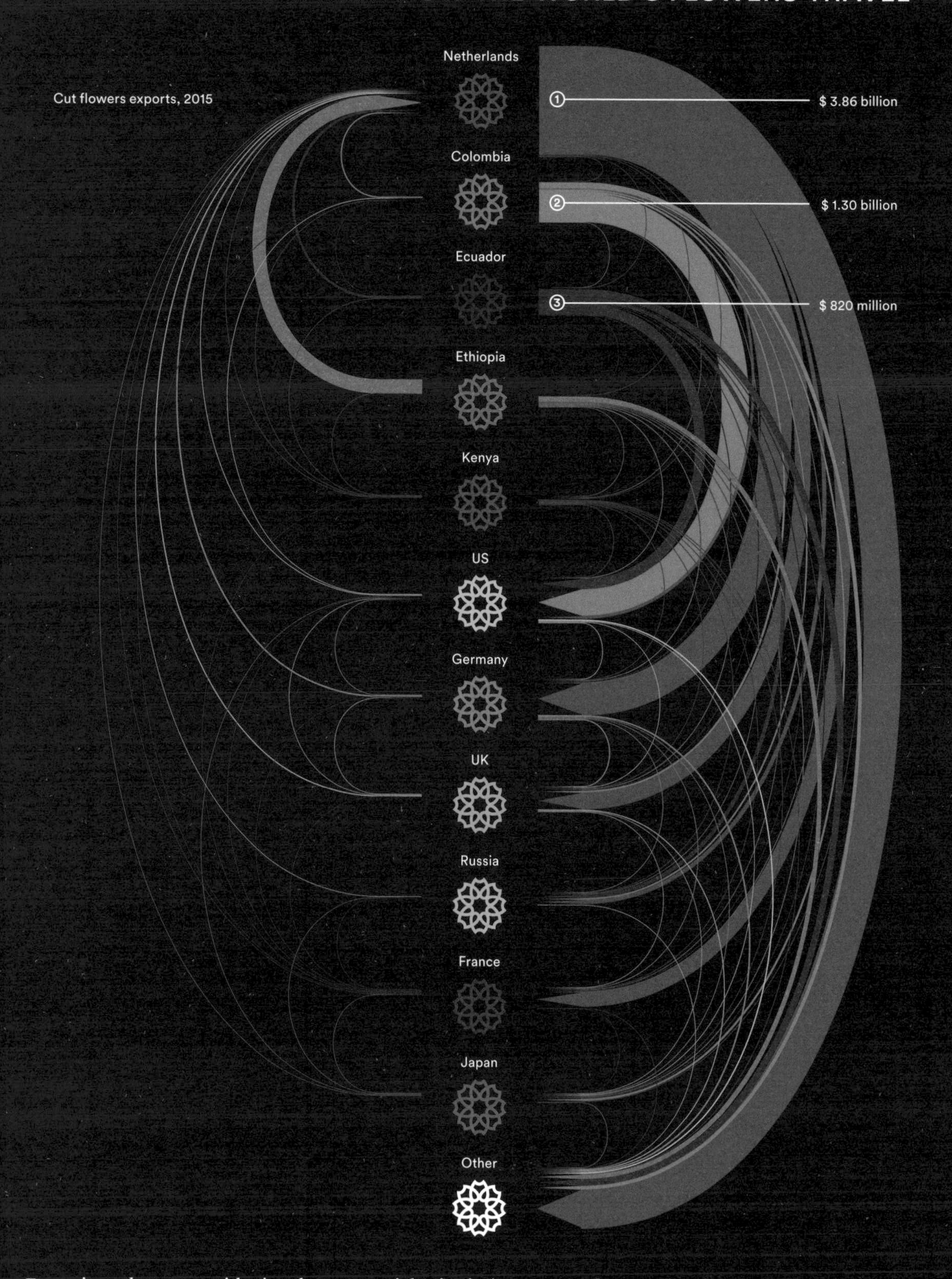

For an item that starts withering the moment it begins its journey, cut flowers often travel a remarkably long way before they are sold to consumers. The US is the largest importer of flowers in the world and its primary suppliers are in the Netherlands, Ecuador, and Colombia, which are also the world's top three exporters. The Netherlands—the largest exporter—ships most of its flowers to its European neighbors, exporting them to countries an average of 590 miles (950 km) away. Colombia sends its crop an average of 3,300 miles away to the UK, Japan, and Canada, as well as the US. And Ecuador's main buyers other than the US are Russia, the Netherlands, and Italy, for an average shipping distance of 4,900 miles. Without refrigerated containers along the way, all those tulips would be dead on arrival. (Data: International Trade Centre)

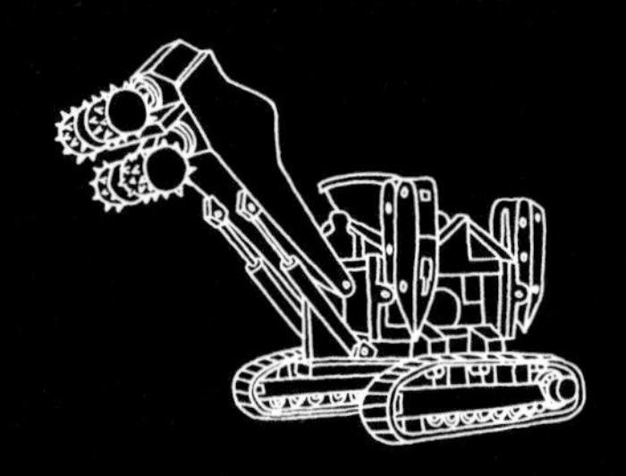

SEABED-MINING MACHINE

Gathering resources for the new global economy

Since ancient Egypt, humans have dug deep into the earth for precious metals and other elements to enhance our edifices, equip us for war, and now power our technologies. With time, our appetite for these minerals has grown—in particular for the so-called "rare earths" vital to everything from batteries to lasers.

Fearful that one day there may not be enough of even the most abundant elements to go around, countries and companies are now racing to lay claim to potential new sources. Some are looking far afield, making plans to mine asteroids and even other planets for elements like platinum and iron. Closer to home, a promising route leads to the deep sea, where we are just beginning to rake copper, diamonds, and phosphorus from the seabed.

The idea of mining the mineral-rich seabed didn't make economic sense when it was first floated decades ago. But recent fears of scarcity, combined with new engineering solutions developed for deepwater oil and gas exploration, have advanced seabed-mining technology. Today, massive unmanned mining machines make it possible to dig in depths that even scientists have not yet explored. Such machines are already gathering diamonds off the coast of Namibia, while others will soon begin deeper excavations off the coast of Papua New Guinea. Dozens of companies have filed for future rights to mine below international waters.

For now, Earth's landmass still holds plenty of the substances we value. But as we cast a prospecting gaze toward areas that once seemed unthinkable, our ambitions challenge the very notion of geopolitics: Who gets first dibs on the ocean's floor? And who the asteroids ED24, SC324, and Ryugu?

↑ Nautilus seabed-mining machine in a fishbowl. (Mathery)

THE UNKNOWABLE RISKS OF MINING FOR RICHES BENEATH THE SEAFLOOR

Under the vast blue that covers two thirds of our planet is an alien world of mouthless worms and saucer-eyed squid whose waters plunge a mile deeper than Mount Everest is tall. And beneath all that is ore—copper, gold, manganese, nickel, cobalt—scattered about the seafloor.

It has been nearly 150 years since seafarers found the first traces of this metallic bounty, but not until 1979 did its sources come to light when an expedition discovered the first hydrothermal vent, or "black smoker."

Where the earth's tectonic plates mash against each other in ocean trenches, the crust cracks. Seawater gushes into these fissures, is heated by magma, and leaches metallic minerals from the crust walls. Like undersea geysers, black smokers spew this searing-hot water back into the ocean above. As it cools, the minerals harden and sink, settling in the sediment. Over time, metallic blankets grow, forming deposits of copper 10 times richer than those on land.

Technology has now put that ore within human reach. But seafloor mining will inevitably destroy lifeforms that live near the vents, such as the scaly-foot gastropod. The deep sea, where much of life on Earth began, has much to teach us about our own origins—and even how life might evolve elsewhere in the universe. Medical breakthroughs await, too: The sea's depths are home to microbes that could be the next antibiotic, fungi that may stave off cancer, and bioluminescent fish whose proteins might light pathways through the human brain.

It's hard to say what's at risk when so little of the deep sea has been explored; there isn't much funding for such research. Some pioneering miners, however, want to work with scientists to test conservation strategies. Scientists don't yet know how to restore the ecosystems that mining might wipe out. Then again, if we don't start somewhere, we'll never find out.

Undersea debut

In 2019, Canadian mining firm Nautilus will debut three huge machines to roam the ocean floor off the coast of Papua New Guinea. CEO Michael Johnston explains:

"The largest copper resource in the world is on the seafloor. There is more copper in the Pacific Ocean than all reserves on land. There's also more nickel, cobalt, and manganese than all reserves on land. And the grades of those deposits are significantly higher than the grades on land. So you have a combination of more resources and higher grade. That's what attracts us.

"The countries that are active in seabed mining—Japan, South Korea, India—are all very large consumers of minerals. Americans, Europeans, and the Chinese are also getting very active.

"The Europeans, for instance, are really quite concerned with the security of their supply. When you talk with planners in the EU, they are concerned because they import every metal. They have technology in Europe, but they're totally dependent. Cellphones [04] and batteries all require metals that are very abundant on the seafloor.

"Everybody who is using a mobile phone, a flat-screen TV, or an iPad is responsible for driving the mining industry to look into these extreme environments."

[04]

The world's appetite for smartphones is insatiable, but the metals needed to make them are finite. According to Yale University professor Thomas Graedel, industry expert Jack Lifton, and Virginia Tech professor Amanda Morris, the metals listed below will be the hardest to replace.

Rhenium and magnesium for metal cases
Rhodium and manganese for printed circuit boards
Lanthanum and yttrium for cellphone cameras
Europium and strontium for color screens
Dysprosium for vibrators
Thulium for electronic filters

↑ A Nautilus seabed-mining machine being built in Newcastle, UK. (May 2014, courtesy of Nautilus)

In 2003, a snail was found living more than 2,500 meters (8,200 ft) below the surface of the Indian Ocean. Thanks to hydrogen sulfide from a nearby seafloor vent, the snail was covered in magnetic iron scales and a biologist noted that the "strange little beast" tended to stick to metal forceps. US scientists have since studied the pliable armor of the scaly-foot gastropod, or *Chrysomallon squamiferum*, for defense applications. Today, both the Indian and Japanese governments

are considering mining their vents for metals, and Nautilus has a dig planned off the coast of Papua New Guinea. But Cindy Lee Van Dover, a marine biologist at Duke University, urges caution. “We don’t know what the tipping point would be—when mining would cause something to go wrong, and we can’t fix it,” she says. “We might lose things before we even know they’re there.” (April 2015, courtesy of Chong Cheng)

CHINA RULES RARE EARTHS

The problem with recycling e-waste

The absolute volume of metals in unwanted electronics globally is tantalizing, says Tom Szaky, CEO of TerraCycle, a New Jersey-based recycling company. But only in theory: "You are definitely able to sell the material at a value more than zero," Szaky says, "but when you count the cost of collecting it, it's a loser."

The problem is the size of the devices: Because they are so small, they have only traces of the metals. If you really want to make some recycling money, Szaky says to skip devices and find yourself an old metal water heater.

"In the Middle East there is oil; in China, there are rare earths," Chinese leader Deng Xiaoping reportedly said in 1992 during his Southern Tour, which marked China's official embrace of market economics. Around that time, China produced about 27% of the world's rare-earth supply. Now it produces about 95%.

From the 1980s and into the new millennium, China's economic agenda has hinged on two priorities: boost exports to acquire foreign currency, and use that foreign currency to develop the advanced technologies of a modern industrial powerhouse. Mining rare earths—essential to most contemporary technologies—has provided an excellent means to achieve these ends. With an estimated 30% of the world's rare-earth reserves, China could supply domestic tech manufacturers and still ship plenty overseas.

Between 1990 and 2000, China's annual production of rare earths increased by about 450%, reaching 73,000 metric tons, according to the US Geological Survey. In the following decade, production increased an additional 70%. Other countries, seduced by China's low prices and burdened by environmental regulations, slowed their own production. By 2011, only 5% of rare-earth production came from outside China, despite the majority of reserves being held elsewhere.

But did this make China the OPEC of rare earths? In 2010, a trade kerfuffle illustrated China's newfound geopolitical leverage—and its limits. In September that year, following a maritime dispute with Japan, China abruptly lowered its export caps on rare earths, causing the price for rare-earth carbonate to skyrocket. But the price jump was short-lived. Investors quickly plowed money into mining projects in the US and Australia, and companies like Hitachi developed technology to improve rare-earth recycling and reduce the use of rare earths in their products. By the time China removed its export cap in 2015, prices for rare earths had sunk.

Despite this, China will likely retain its competitive advantage in the rare-earths industry. For one thing, mining companies there aren't subject to the expensive environmental controls that bind projects in the US and elsewhere. Plus, opening up new mines requires considerable capital investment and up to seven years of preparation. Meanwhile, the market size for rare-earth elements was valued at just $4-$6 billion as of 2015, meaning it may not warrant enough investor attention to fund new mines. If China wants to keep foreign rivals away from its practical monopoly, all it has to do is keep supplying them.

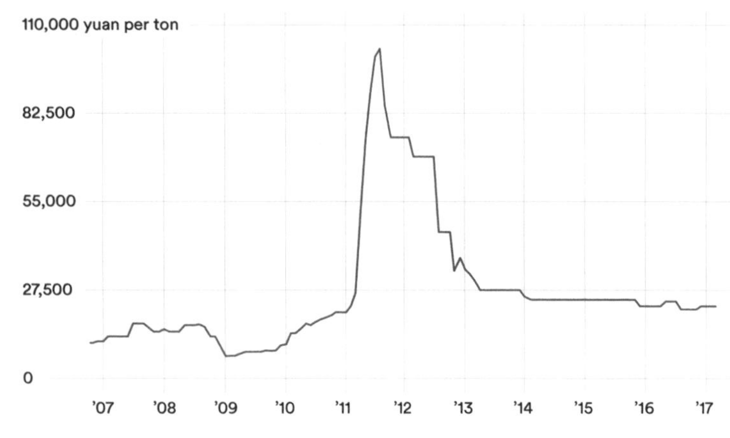

↑ Price of rare-earth carbonate (yuan per metric ton).
Data: Wind Datafeed Service

THE BEST DIAMONDS IN THE WORLD ARE BURIED IN MUD AT THE BOTTOM OF THE ATLANTIC OCEAN

The best diamonds in the world come from the sea. Swept up from riverbeds by the mighty Orange River in southern Africa back when dinosaurs still roamed the earth, their bumpy journey to the Atlantic Ocean polished them and broke up any stones with flaws, ensuring only the strongest and best survived.

Those diamonds landed off the coast of what is now Namibia, creating the world's richest marine-diamond deposit. The country's territorial waters are now estimated to hold 80 million carats, and the world's biggest diamond miner, De Beers, has quietly built up an armada off the coast to vacuum up those precious gems.

Diamonds on land are running out; no economically viable new source has been found in 20 years. Mines in Canada and Australia could run out in five years, analysts say, and Botswana, home to De Beers' sales headquarters, will be bare by 2030. Business consultancy Bain has predicted that even with bountiful sources like Russia and Namibia, the global supply of rough diamonds will decline by 2% per year until 2030.

That decline would be even faster if not for undersea jewels. Debmarine, De Beers' exclusive joint venture with the Namibian government, says 60% of local Namibian diamonds currently come from the sea and predicts that could soon rise to 94%. Since undersea mining began 14 years ago, 16 million carats have been mined at sea and 62 million on land in Namibia.

Debmarine uses five vessels fitted with either drills or a giant "tractor" that sucks up sediment from the seabed. This is passed through filters and x-rays to separate out the gems. The tractor alone hoovers up 630 metric tons of material every hour, yielding around 80 carats, which is a palmful of stones.

Plenty of other miners are following Debmarine's example: Twenty-six seabed-mining licenses have been granted to firms from various countries for sites in the Pacific's international waters.

De Beers' parent company, Anglo American, owns shares in Nautilus and will be watching these early explorations with interest. It might also soon have company on the Namibian seabed: In October 2016, the first phosphate-mining firm got government permission to start exploring the deep sea.

Security on a diamond trawler

No human hands touch marine diamonds as they are sucked up from the seabed and dispatched through a series of filters on Debmarine's customized mining ships in Namibia. The zone in which the stones are processed is called the "red area," and all but a small number of the ship's crew are forbidden to enter.

Once X-rays confirm the stones are diamonds, they are machine-sealed in tin cans, barcoded, and whisked along a conveyer belt to a safe to await collection. Three times a week, these cans are loaded into James Bond-style metal briefcases and transported to land by helicopter.

A single stolen diamond undermines a mining company's guarantee of provenance to consumers. The industry has been blighted in the past by controversy over illicitly mined blood diamonds, traded for weapons in conflicts across Africa. Trust has only been regained with the introduction of tight security controls.

"It's a bit nerve-wracking at first, but you get used to it," says James van Vyk, a security officer aboard one of the ships. "We rarely actually see diamonds here."

↑ A pile of uncut diamonds in 1955 in Oranjemund, Namibia. Debmarine sorts its diamonds in the same town today. (Photo by Volkmar K. Wentzel/National Geographic/Getty)

• Lithium

Lithium is the central element in batteries for smartphones, laptops, and electric cars. Researchers are working to create a more energetic battery, but lithium continues to be the only element with the potential to power our newest devices. Pictured: Lepidolite, K(Li,Al)3(Si,Al)4O10(F,OH)2

• Carbon

As carbon processing improves, new properties emerge for chemical sensors, healthcare diagnostics, renewable-energy technologies, and lightweight composites for both auto and aerospace transportation. Carbon processing also controls atomic arrangements from nanotubes to more familiar structures such as graphite and diamond. Pictured: Azurite, Cu3(CO3)2(OH)2

• Aluminum

Aluminum is in everything, including vehicles, packaging, construction materials, electrical-transmission lines, electronics, and LEDs, and is also used in water treatment and petroleum refining. It is lightweight and resists corrosion: These two properties alone solidify its importance in industrial applications. Pictured: Bauxite, Al2O3·nH2O

• Silicon

Silicon has been the workhorse of electronics in communication and computer components since the 1960s. New ways of wedding it with other materials could produce structures that sense, communicate data, and harvest energy. Pictured: Opal, SiO2·n(H2O)

• Phosphorus

Phosphorus is the key to fertilizer, along with nitrogen and potassium. Inorganic chemical fertilizers including processed phosphates are central to food production and their cost and availability directly affect food costs. Pictured: Torbernite, Cu(UO2)2(PO4)2·8-12 H2O

• Titanium

This element has gone from research use for military aircraft in World War II to commercial use in today's shape-memory alloys—which are combined with nickel—in arterial stents, golf clubs, dental wires, and eyeglass frames. Pictured: Titanite, CaTiSiO5

• Iron

Steel—alloyed with carbon—has been mass-produced since the mid 1800s. It remains the dominant metal used in infrastructure from buildings to bridges. Pictured: Goethite, FeO(OH)

• Cobalt

In the 2010s, a crisis erupted over a perceived shortage of this transition metal, necessary to manufacture lithium-ion batteries. It passed, but demand will surge again with rising need for batteries in portable electronics, vehicles, and power-grid storage. Pictured: Cobaltite, CoAsS

• Zinc

Zinc is key in the blue LEDs whose inventors won the 2014 Nobel prize in physics, completing the visual spectrum of LEDs for energy-efficient lighting, displays, and non-fossil-fuel lighting. Pictured: Smithsonite, ZnCO3

• Gallium

Blue LEDs with high brightness and efficiency were ultimately achieved with gallium nitride. Gallium arsenide is also in red LEDs and the solar panels of the Mars Rover. Pictured, Renierite with silver flecks of Gallite, CuGaS2

• Selenium

Selenium is used in night-vision goggles and more commonly as an additive in glass for tinting. It can also be used in solar cells, but that's not as common yet. Battery scientists are experimenting with selenium to break through current capacity constraints. Pictured: Native selenium, Se

THE MOST IMPORTANT ELEMENTS FOR THE NEW GLOBAL ECONOMY

List written by Krystyn van Vliet, MIT professor of materials science, with contributions by Amanda Morris, chemistry professor at Virginia Tech University. (Photos courtesy of Harvard Geological Museum and Element Collection)

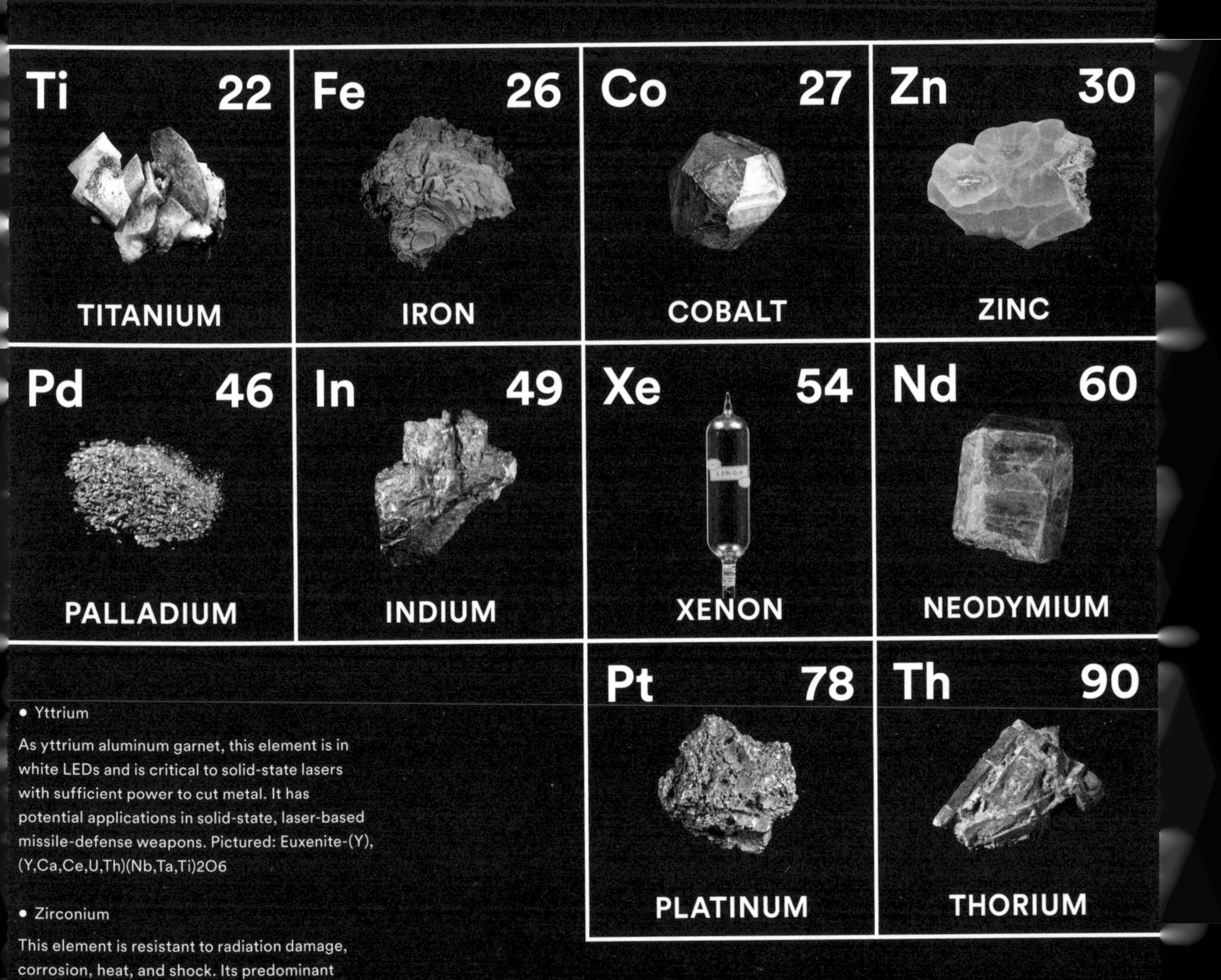

- Yttrium

As yttrium aluminum garnet, this element is in white LEDs and is critical to solid-state lasers with sufficient power to cut metal. It has potential applications in solid-state, laser-based missile-defense weapons. Pictured: Euxenite-(Y), (Y,Ca,Ce,U,Th)(Nb,Ta,Ti)2O6

- Zirconium

This element is resistant to radiation damage, corrosion, heat, and shock. Its predominant use is in nuclear reactors as a metallic alloy for tubing. It is also widely used in chemical and water processing and in industrial and aerospace furnaces. Pictured: Zircon, ZrSiO4

- Palladium

After years of attempts to replace this expensive element, palladium is still a great catalyst material. Used in catalytic converters and in fuel cells, it is also a key layer in capacitors for cellphones and laptops. Pictured: Palladium, Pd

- Indium

Indium is the key element in indium tin oxide, essential to photovoltaics, flat-panel displays, smart windows, and organic LEDs.
The transparent, conductive nature of this material can make an aircraft-windshield coating that heats up to melt ice. Pictured: Sakuraiite

- Xenon

This gas is used in photography lights and, because it is bacteriocidal, in food preparation. It is also a fuel for ion-thruster propulsion systems for satellites in orbit and on the International Space Station. Pictured: Xenon gas in a flask

- Neodymium

This magnetic material is in the electric motors of power tools, wind turbines, sensors and actuators in hard drives, and MRI machines. It is also used in audio speakers, door locks, and toys. Pictured: Monazite-(Ce), (Ce, La, Nd, Th)

- Platinum

Platinum is expensive, but it's the best metal catalyst and is used in optical fibers and chemotherapies. A few grams in a car's catalytic converter can neutralize noxious engine emissions. Pictured: Native platinum, Pt

- Thorium

Thorium is a potential fuel for nuclear-power plants. Thorium reactors are cheaper to operate than conventional nuclear plants and produce shorter-lived radioactive waste. India has already invested in thorium-reactor research and technology. Pictured: Thorite (Th,U)SiO4

↑ Quartz (SiO_2) is the second most abundant mineral on the surface of the earth after feldspar. Quartz (qz.com) is a digitally native news outlet, born in 2012, for business people in the new global economy. (Courtesy of the Mineralogical & Geological Museum at Harvard University)

SEARCHING FOR SCRAPS OF GOLD IN SOUTH AFRICA'S ABANDONED MINES

Clean-shaven and wearing pressed trousers, Vusumuzi and Ndumiso are above ground for the first time in four days. Like thousands of others, they are illegal miners, secretly digging for scraps in the abandoned gold mines of Johannesburg.

The two men, both in their thirties, describe their operation: Men line up for days outside an abandoned mine shaft, patiently waiting for a turn to chip away at the rock within. No one has helmets or emergency equipment. Once back on the surface, they go to a nearby stream to crush the rock into a fine powder and strain it through a handkerchief. They use liquid mercury, heedless of its danger, to transform these gold flakes into a sellable lump.

↑ Gold ingot from a mine in Kinross, South Africa. (March 1994. Photo by Brooks Kraft LLC/Sygma/Getty)

A good dig (about 60 grams of gold or 1.9 troy ounces) can bring in about 30,000 rand ($2,300), Vusumuzi says. Their last dig yielded only 17,400 rand, which when split among their team of 14 equalled around $95 each. Most of that is sent to their families in Zimbabwe.

Ndumiso says he has sold his gold to teachers, policemen, South Africans, and foreigners. They, in turn, may sell to bulk buyers. Through corrupt export companies, the gold is sent to an internationally recognized refinery where it is mixed with legitimate gold and sold on the international market.

This cottage industry is so confident that it now operates in the open. In one abandoned former gold-mining town, women grind rock inside the ruins of what was likely once a mine manager's house while men stand guard nearby. And near a busy intersection in western Johannesburg, worn shoes, car headlights, and discarded clothes mark the location of another illegal mine entrance, leading to tunnels as deep as four km (2.5 miles).

In South Africa, illegal mining of gold and other minerals like diamonds and chrome is worth about $530 million each year, about one tenth of the value of the country's gold exports. Its five tiers—underground miners, individual buyers, bulk buyers, national distributors, and international dealers—make it hard for the authorities to stop the trade, according to the Chamber of Mines.

The country's black-market gold rush started in the early 2000s when commodity prices took off. It persisted as the gold price in rand remained strong, even when its price in US dollars was unsteady. Today, it's a solid investment in an uncertain global economy.

Bacteria are miners, too

If mining ever becomes fully environmentally friendly, energy-efficient, safe, and waste-free, it may be thanks to ancient lifeforms called lithotrophs, microorganisms that "eat" inorganic compounds to survive. They break down minerals in rock, usually by oxidizing the sulfur or iron within them and thus releasing metals.

In northern Chile, the Biosigma lab has been injecting bacteria into low-grade copper-ore waste since 2012. The process, called bioleaching, is behind roughly 20% of the world's global copper production. At mining sites in South Africa, similar bacteria are currently liberating fine particles of gold from sulfide minerals. And in 2016, scientists at the National University of Singapore successfully re-engineered *Chromobacterium violaceum*, which normally lives on soil nutrients, to extract precious metals from cellphones.

Bacteria may one day teach scientists how to mine plants for metals absorbed in their roots; point to undiscovered mineral reserves deep underground; or even transform waste into riches. Biologists at McMaster University in Hamilton, Canada discovered a bacterium in 2013 that, when placed in toxic, water-soluble gold, "poops" solid gold nuggets. They say it could eventually be deployed in waste piles and left alone to play King Midas.

Translation, counterclockwise:

This is the head

This is the neck
The neck
The neck of a man
What is this?

This is the shoulder
The shoulder
This is the shoulder
What is this?

This is the arm
This is your arm
The arm
What is this?

This is the fingers
This is the fingers
This is the fingers
This is the fingers
What's this?

This is the leg
The leg
The leg of a man
Your leg
What's this?

The knee
This is the knee
What's this?

What is this?

This is the shoulder

The body
This is his body
What's this?

This is the elbow
This is his elbow
What's this?

The knee
This is the knee
What's this?

These are the toes.

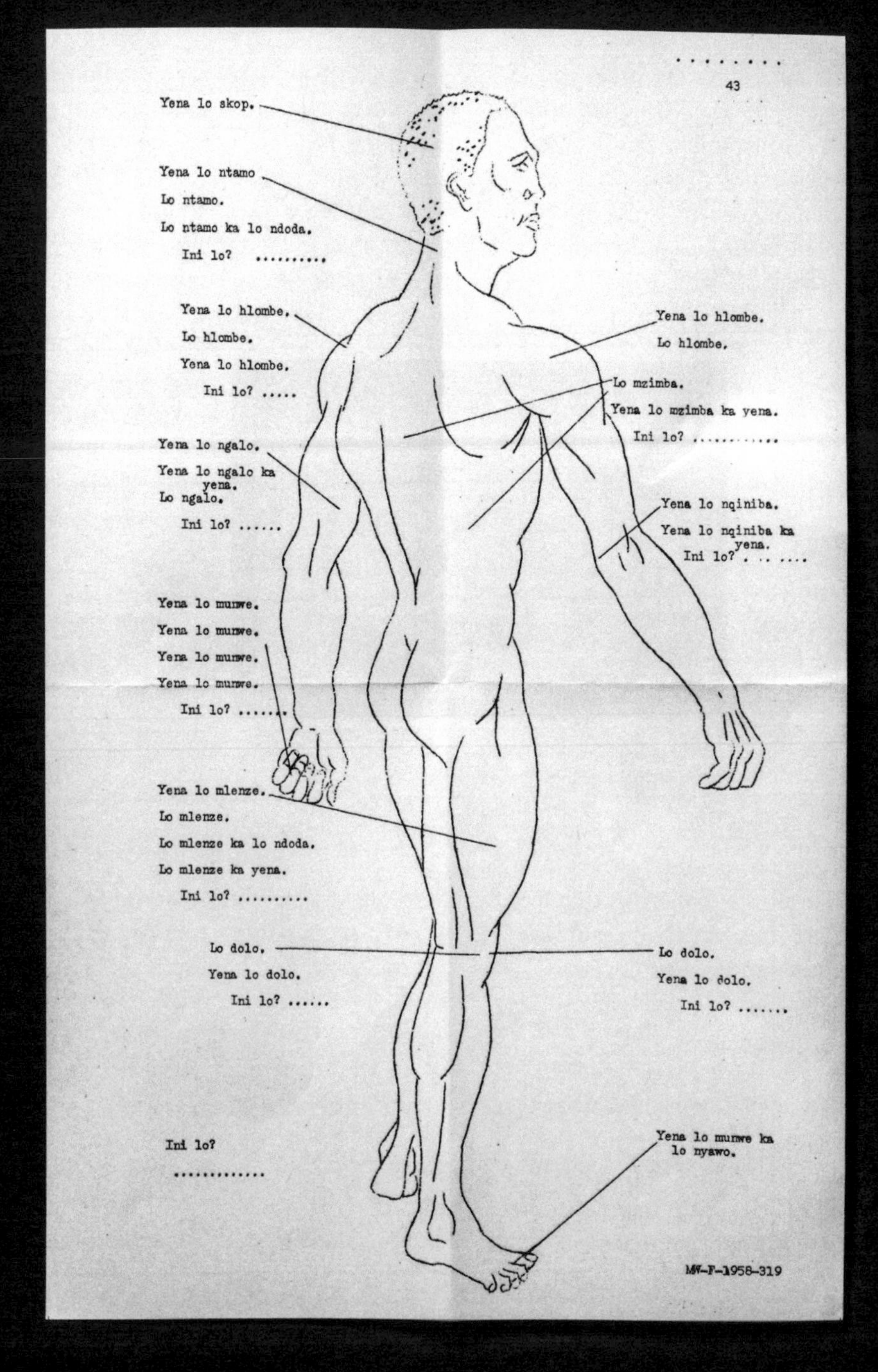

Fanakalo is a language of racial hierarchy. Invented in the early 1900s by white South African mine owners, the pidgin tongue marries African vocabularies such as isiZulu to the grammatical structure of English. Simple and unambiguous, it was designed to give and receive orders on mining sites where migrant African workers and their European supervisors struggled to find a common tongue. Fanakalo used to be taught to miners in classrooms, always with an eye toward inculcating obedience. As one 1957 Fanakalo primer for mine managers advised, "Questions of the type 'Didn't you do this?' [and] 'Haven't you finished?' should be avoided as much as possible, because whether the answer is given as 'yes' or 'no,' ambiguity may result." Mining employs 5% of South Africa's formal labor force today, according to government statistics. Fanakalo has fallen somewhat out of fashion, no longer complex enough to match technological advances in the mining industry. However, in 2008, researchers at the University of the Witwatersrand found that it was still the lingua franca in mines where laborers did not speak the same native language. In cities, traces of Fanakalo can still be heard wherever unskilled, low-paid labor is negotiated. (Page from a 1958 training manual for South Africa's Chamber of Mines. Courtesy of the Historical Papers Research Archive at the University of the Witwatersrand)

IRIS SCANNER

Securing borders in a post-national world

Your irises will soon be your keys to the world. The use of iris scanners—small, affordable cameras that turn the intricate patterns on the human eye into a unique personal code—has exploded in recent years. One analysis predicted the market would grow by more than 21% a year between 2016 and 2020.

In Jordan, they're helping refugees get cash from biometric ATMs. In India, iris scans are collected as part of the country's massive citizen-identification drive, Aadhaar. At Google, engineers get scanned in order to access the company's secure data centers. At Samsung, the ill-fated Galaxy Note 7 was one of the first smartphones that could unlock by recognizing its owner's iris.

The purpose of these and other biometrics is simple: Figure out if people are, in fact, who they say they are. Since the patterns on our irises change very little, a scan taken shortly after birth can be used decades later to let you onto a plane or either convict or acquit you of a crime. And because current technology can capture iris patterns up to 12 meters (39 ft) away, it's already easy for a camera to identify everyone in a room—or a train carriage, *Minority Report*-style.

The scanners aren't foolproof, however: Researchers have reverse-engineered contact lenses that trick the machines into picking up false patterns. Of course it's harder for criminals to replace their irises than it is for them to dye their hair, shave their beards, or find a fake passport. But as biometric technologies evolve, so will the tools to bypass them—and the machines will be none the wiser. After all, from a scanner's point of view, we are all just a series of numbers to be read.

↑ Woman using a Trident iris scanner. (Mathery)

HOW INDIA BUILT THE BIGGEST BIOMETRIC DATABASE IN THE WORLD

For decades, India has suffered from a debilitating leak. The country spends trillions of rupees (tens of billions of US dollars) on subsidies for fuel, food, fertilizers, and other kinds of assistance, but rarely more than a quarter reaches the poor it's meant for due to middlemen, systemic inefficiencies, and corruption.

In 2009, the Indian government decided to fix this mess by giving all 1.2 billion Indians an identity number linked to their biometric data. It was hoped that the 12-digit number would weed out fake beneficiaries,[05] improve accountability, and give millions of Indians their first universally held form of official identification. The number was christened "Aadhaar," meaning "foundation" or "base" in Hindi.

"The heart of the problem was, 'How do we get a billion people to be unique?'" explains Nandan Nilekani, a tech billionaire who joined the government for the project. Nilekani was put in charge of the Unique Identification Authority of India (UIDAI), which was established in 2009 to run the Aadhaar program. Over the next seven years, the UIDAI would generate over a billion Aadhaar numbers.

That meant creating the largest biometric identification system in the world. To do so in India—with its massive hinterland, low internet penetration, and dismal literacy rates—was a huge technological and logistical task.

Most biometric systems, such as those used at border crossings, are designed to identify suspicious persons. But Aadhaar exists to identify the unidentified. Nilekani says the UIDAI aimed to "create a system where we take somebody's biometrics, compare them against all the people we have, and if that person's biometrics are not there, then treat that person as a new person and assign a number to him."

To cheaply gather quality biometrics from citizens, UIDAI did some *jugaad*, India's beloved term for low-cost innovation. It prescribed standards for three biometric collection devices: a camera, fingerprint scanner, and iris scanner.[06] Vendors competed to sell products meeting these standards to enrollment agencies, which in turn competed to be hired to register citizens. Creating this competitive marketplace for devices and services within the Aadhaar program allowed UIDAI to slash costs: From an initial estimate of Rs100 ($1.50) per Aadhaar number per person, the price came to Rs60-70.

Today, Indians use Aadhaar for everything from getting basic subsidies to identity verification on marriage websites. "Before Aadhaar, the largest fingerprint system was the FBI's, with about 100 million individuals. And now we have Aadhaar with 1 billion," says Anil Jain, a professor at Michigan State University and a biometric expert. "Nobody could even imagine such a system would be available and be successful." And definitely not in India.

[05] In Mexico City, biometrics are already making life easier for public-service pensioners. Once forced to travel to a central bank every six months for "proof of life," pensioners can now prevent fraud and keep collecting government checks by phoning in "voice prints."

[06] The iris-recognition business, worth less than $700 million in 2016, will expand to $4.1 billion by 2025, predicts market-research firm Tractica. Demand will balloon for iris-based identification for personal devices, prescription-drug dispensation, and ATMs, among other products and services.

↑ A man applying for an Aadhaar card in New Delhi has his iris scanned. (April 12, 2013, Priyanka Parashar/Mint via Getty)

BIOMETRIC ID CARDS IN THE UNITED ARAB EMIRATES DEFINE WHO DOESN'T BELONG

In 2004, the Emirates Identity Authority embarked on an ambitious project to digitize the identity documents of Emirati citizens, long-term residents, and short-term workers. Over the next decade, it put together a biometric database of around 140 million fingerprints, palm and hand prints, digital signatures, and facial scans[07] belonging to people of more than 200 nationalities.

For a government, the arguments in favor of such a database are legion. Biometrics help secure borders near war zones (in this case, Syria) and speed up screening at airports. They provide the authorities with an exhaustive tally of the population. And they can help expel foreigners who break the law.[08]

But there's something else lurking beneath the data: an attempt to define who belongs, and who doesn't. "A new technology enables the state to reimagine itself," says Yoana Kuzmova, a lawyer who works with stateless people in the UAE—those whom no government will recognize as citizens. "When you digitize a record or personal ID, it's a convenient time to leave someone out." In other words, the routine collection of records could later serve to deny someone the right to live, work, or participate in a society.

This has happened before. Historically, Gulf societies were mobile and tribal, not fixed and national. When their current borders were drawn in the 20th century, tens of thousands of people either had no chance to register as citizens or didn't know how. The technology back then was decidedly analog, Kuzmova says: It took the form of state surveys and genealogical "family books" written on paper. But these records, or the lack of them, would later serve to deny people nationality.

It was hard enough for these young countries to establish a coherent national identity, and their large populations of foreign workers—from well-off Western expats to low-paid South Asian laborers—now make it even harder. Their lack of democracy also means less civic participation, which is another key component of national identity.

So what does it mean to be Emirati or Kuwaiti today? The most basic marker of belonging might simply be a person's deportability. One goal of the UAE's biometric initiative was to prevent foreigners who'd been deported from re-entering on false documents. The six countries of the Gulf Cooperation Council plan to share the data, so someone expelled from one country cannot enter another.[09]

This allows the state to "reimagine itself" in a very real sense. When everyone is identifiable, borders between states may no longer be necessary: They'll be drawn around people instead.

[07]
To thwart toilet-paper thieves in the public restrooms of Beijing's Temple of Heaven Park, officials installed a dispenser equipped with facial-recognition software in 2017. Visitors must register their faces to receive a two-foot ration.

[08]
Biometrics can spot a liar: A body-scanning kiosk that picks up even subtle movements, like the curling of one's toes, is now being tested by Canadian border police. Like human officers, it conducts routine interviews with would-be entrants.

[09]
Biometrics aren't just about keeping people in or out: After the 2014 crash of AirAsia Flight QZ8501, mobile fingerprint readers allowed Indonesian officials to identify deceased victims. Japanese researchers have also developed a hand-scanning system to identify elderly people who may not be able to communicate.

THE WORLD'S MOST POWERFUL PASSPORTS, RANKED BY ACCESS TO GLOBAL FINANCIAL CENTERS

Your passport is only as good as the places it can take you. This page ranks the world's passports not by how many countries their holders can access without a visa, but by how many international economic hotspots holders can access, from London to Shenzhen to the Cayman Islands. By this measure, the world's most powerful passport turns out to be San Marino. The tiny Mediterranean republic offers its 33,200 citizens visa-free access not only to dynamic European and US cities but also to China's many fast-growing metropolises, thanks to a unique pact between one of the largest and one of the smallest countries in the world. (Based on the 2016 Global Financial Centers Index, compiled by London-based consultancy Z/Yen. Passport photos from Wikimedia Commons, Quartz, Shutterstock, and Getty)

A MEETING AFTER WORLD WAR I DETERMINED THE SIZE AND SHAPE OF EVERY PASSPORT IN THE WORLD

The chip hacker

Adam Laurie is the founder of UK-based security research firm Aperture Labs. He is an expert in cloning RFID chips, which are embedded in everything from passports to pets.

"Depending on which country you come from, the amount of data stored in the RFID chip on your passport varies. The mandatory information is all the details printed on the picture page of the passport, plus the digital picture, which is used for facial recognition.

"The digital picture has a digital signature—something that proves it was created by an official body, like the British government. It is possible to verify the signature in order to know that the image has not been tampered with. But someone cloning the chip could also update the signature.

"The only way to check if the digital signature is valid is by using the Public Key Directory, which tells you if the signing key is actually a valid signing key for that country.

"The problem is that being a member of the PKD is not mandatory, and some countries issuing electronic passports are not members. So if I want to forge a passport, I could just pick a country that's not a member of the PKD.

"The simplest way to make passports more secure would be to make membership of the PKD mandatory."

On Oct. 21, 1920, the League of Nations convened in France for a meeting that would shape modern travel. After World War I, easing border crossings by train was a priority, but the lack of a standardized passport design posed "a serious obstacle to the resumption of normal intercourse and to the economic recovery of the world," the League noted. Border officials struggled to scrutinize foreign certifications of dizzying shapes and sizes, with sometimes partial information and little guidance as to what was authentic.

The Paris Conference on Passports & Customs Formalities and Through Tickets specified the size, layout, and design of travel documents for 42 nations. It ratified the template for a 32-page booklet exactly 15.5 cm x 10.5 cm (6.1 inches x 4.1 inches) with the first four pages detailing the bearer's facial characteristics, occupation, and residence. Assuming that travelers were married males traveling with their families, the layout included a box for a photo of the bearer's spouse and space for the names of his children. Each passport was to be in French and at least one other language; its cardboard cover would have the country's name and coat of arms centered on it; and the document should cost no more than 10 francs.

Although now governed by standards set by the UN's International Civil Aviation Organization, passport layouts have remained much the same for nearly 100 years. But the invisible technology that secures them has greatly advanced, including layers of watermarks, holograms, disappearing inks, perforated numbers, fluorescent threads, embossed letters, see-through registers, and book-binding techniques. Most notably, a small rectangular icon on the cover ( ) denotes the presence of a microchip containing the bearer's biometric data. Now widespread, the ePassport was pioneered by the Malaysian government, which has been using microchips invented by a Kuala Lumpur-based biometric company, IRIS Corporation, since 1998.

However, the passport booklet itself may soon become obsolete. Australia is already testing a face-scanning-based system called "Seamless Traveller" that will eliminate the need for most travelers to show passports at borders by 2020. Like the League of Nations passport committee a century ago, officials hope the system will ease queues and "transform the border experience" for travelers. But the small magic of having a nostalgic, pocket-sized record of one's travels will be lost.

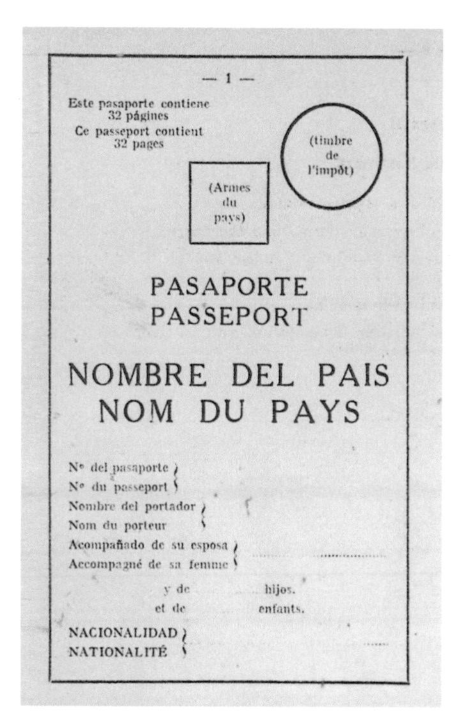

— 1 —

Este pasaporte contiene
32 páginas
Ce passeport contient
32 pages

(Armes du pays)

(timbre de l'impôt)

PASAPORTE
PASSEPORT

NOMBRE DEL PAIS
NOM DU PAYS

Nº del pasaporte
Nº du passeport

Nombre del portador
Nom du porteur

Acompañado de su esposa
Accompagné de sa femme

y de .... hijos.
et de .... enfants.

NACIONALIDAD
NATIONALITÉ

↑ Model passport proposed by the League of Nations' Advisory and Technical Committee for Communications and Transit in November 1925. (Courtesy of New York Public Library)

THE SECRETS OF THE WORLD'S MOST SECURE PASSPORT

Security ink

The passport uses at least four types of security inks: intaglio, infrared, ultraviolet, and Gemini or fluorescent ink. These reveal patterns under certain kinds of light.

Bright fibers

Color-changing fibers are embedded through the document's pulp. They look blue and red in daylight and change to various bright colors under UV lighting.

Microtext portraiture

The bearer's portrait is repeated on the document's third page. A magnifying loupe reveals that this image is made up of tiny letters and numbers corresponding to the bearer's name and date of birth.

Glow-in-the-dark binding

A twisted string of red, white, and blue sewing thread is used in the binding.

Watermarks

Every visa page has a watermark of William Shakespeare, and the bio page contains a watermark of a historic sailboat and four flowers. The passport also uses a watermarking feature called Skylight (developed by its printer, De La Rue of Basingstoke) that appears as small dots across the page.

Perforated numbers

A unique nine-digit serial number is lasered throughout the booklet.

Hologram

The plastic laminate over the passport's biographic page contains a patterned image that appears when the passport is tilted.

Numbering

Beneath the bearer's photo is a small patch of clear film that is printed with a unique seven-character alphanumeric sequence followed by a checkmark symbol.

Tell-tale construction

The biodata page is the most tampered-with section of a passport. A new construction technique was designed to expose any attempts to alter it. The laminated page summarizing the bearer's personal details is now printed on one continuous sheet that is glued to the inside-back cover. Tearing off this page will damage the entire booklet.

The United Kingdom claims to have the world's most secure passport. Updated every five years, its design features nationalistic collages and a hodgepodge of graphical tricks to foil counterfeiters. To help untrained checkers, the 2015 version even has a page summarizing the document's visible security features. (Courtesy of UK Home Office)

BORN WITHOUT FINGERPRINTS

Cheryl Maynard, 53, of Fairfax, Virginia has dermatopathia pigmentosa reticularis *(DPR), a rare condition that erases any sign of fingerprints from the skin.* "I'm the fifth generation in my family to have this condition. So when I was born, my parents knew there was a good chance I was going to have it. The first time I went overseas I was nearly two years old. We were going to Germany. Of course they had to fingerprint everybody in the family. They tried and they tried again, and nothing would come of it. Eventually we started getting letters from doctors saying that we didn't have fingerprints. It's always kind of been a party trick, but it wasn't that much of an issue until I went to get a security clearance of my own. When I worked for an airline, it had to do a background check on everyone. Everybody in my class of flight attendants had their check done in seven to 10 days. My background check took almost six weeks. I bought a Motorola Droid recently. When I was in the store, I asked the vendor what the thing on the bottom part of the phone was. I thought it was the power button, but the salesman said it was actually the fingerprint lock. I just started laughing." (Feb. 27, 2017, Stephen Voss for Quartz)

HOW AN ALGORITHM RECOGNIZES YOUR FACE

We still don't know exactly how humans recognize faces, but to an algorithm, your face is nothing more than a list of numbers.

A high-resolution image may have tens of millions of pixels. To scan all of them to look for the patterns of pixels that make a face would take far too much time and computing power. So instead of representing the data directly, early artificial intelligence considered only the relationships between blocks of pixels. These relationships are represented by numbers that indicate a change in color and the direction of that change.

Lists of these numbers could represent the curve of an eyebrow or the dimple of a chin. This technique has many benefits: The algorithm doesn't need to store original photos for reference, which saves a lot of space because it can learn from thousands or millions of images. It also helps when photos of one person vary in brightness or by the angle of their face to the camera.

But how does an algorithm know what makes one person unique? Researchers at Google found the best way was to let it decide for itself. In 2015, the Google team coded a learning algorithm called FaceNet to recognize a small set of people, making the bot analyze hundreds of photos of each person's face. The algorithm then determined on its own which patterns were common to them. When the algorithm locked down a set of relationships that described a certain face, it compared any new face to those numbers. If the numbers matched up, the machine decided it was the same person.

Because of this simple idea, it's now possible to instantly surveil every passenger walking through an airport or immediately identify anyone recorded by a police body camera. It has even trickled down to consumer electronics, where your face can unlock Windows laptops and Samsung phones.

Facial recognition changes what it means to be in public and how much we know about where people are at any given time. The value of privacy and anonymity are about to be tested. Does that cost outweigh the potential to deter crime or find a lost child?

Film school

Biometric identification has been used in film to illustrate a future filled with ease and convenience as well as showcase dystopian surveillance states. But both of these visions of the future can look increasingly quaint as even more advanced versions appear in real life.

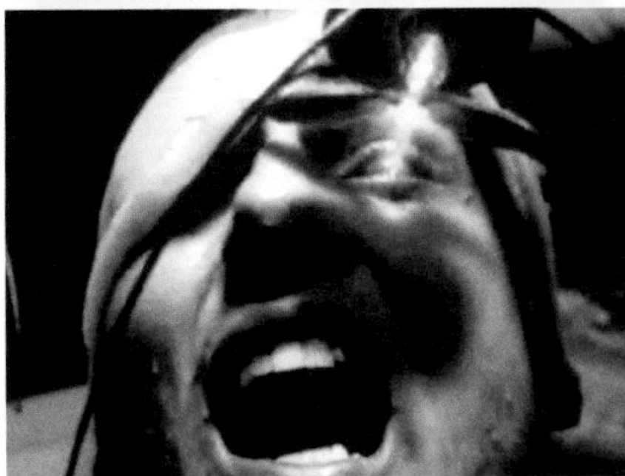

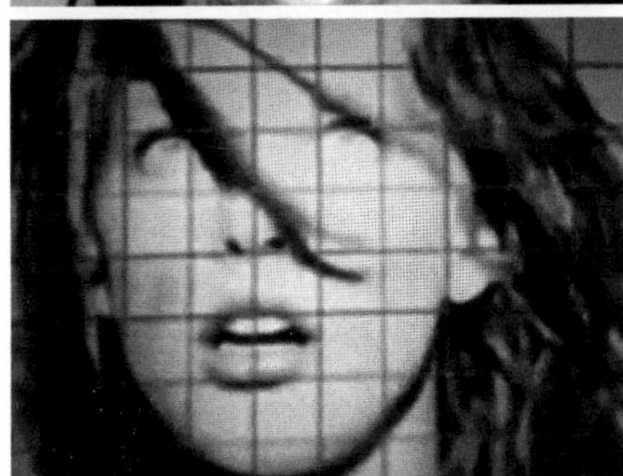

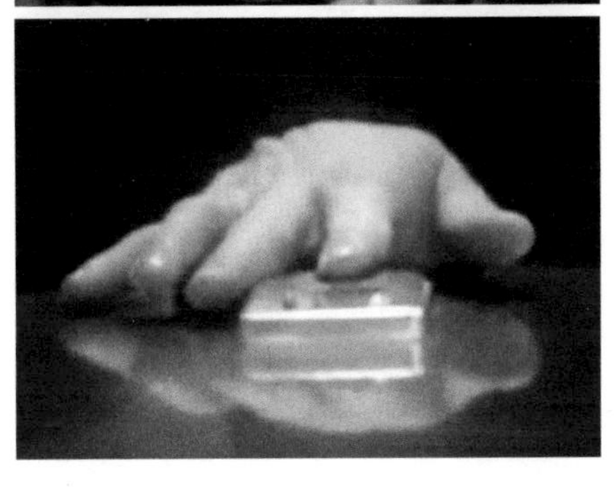

From top to bottom:

The seamless thumbprint payment in *Back to the Future Part II* (1989, Universal Pictures) has been surpassed by smile-activated payments to Alibaba in real life. Facial analysis used by police in *Minority Report* (2002, 20th Century Fox) and *the Fifth Element* (1997, Gaumont) is now *de rigeur* in law enforcement. Meanwhile, blood tests to prove identity, as once seen in *Gattaca* (1997, Columbia Pictures), are a little less sophisticated than the DNA tests used to today both incriminate and exonerate.

SCARRED, SCRATCHED, DISTORTED, AND OBSCURED: THE SCIENCE OF FINGERPRINT DETECTION

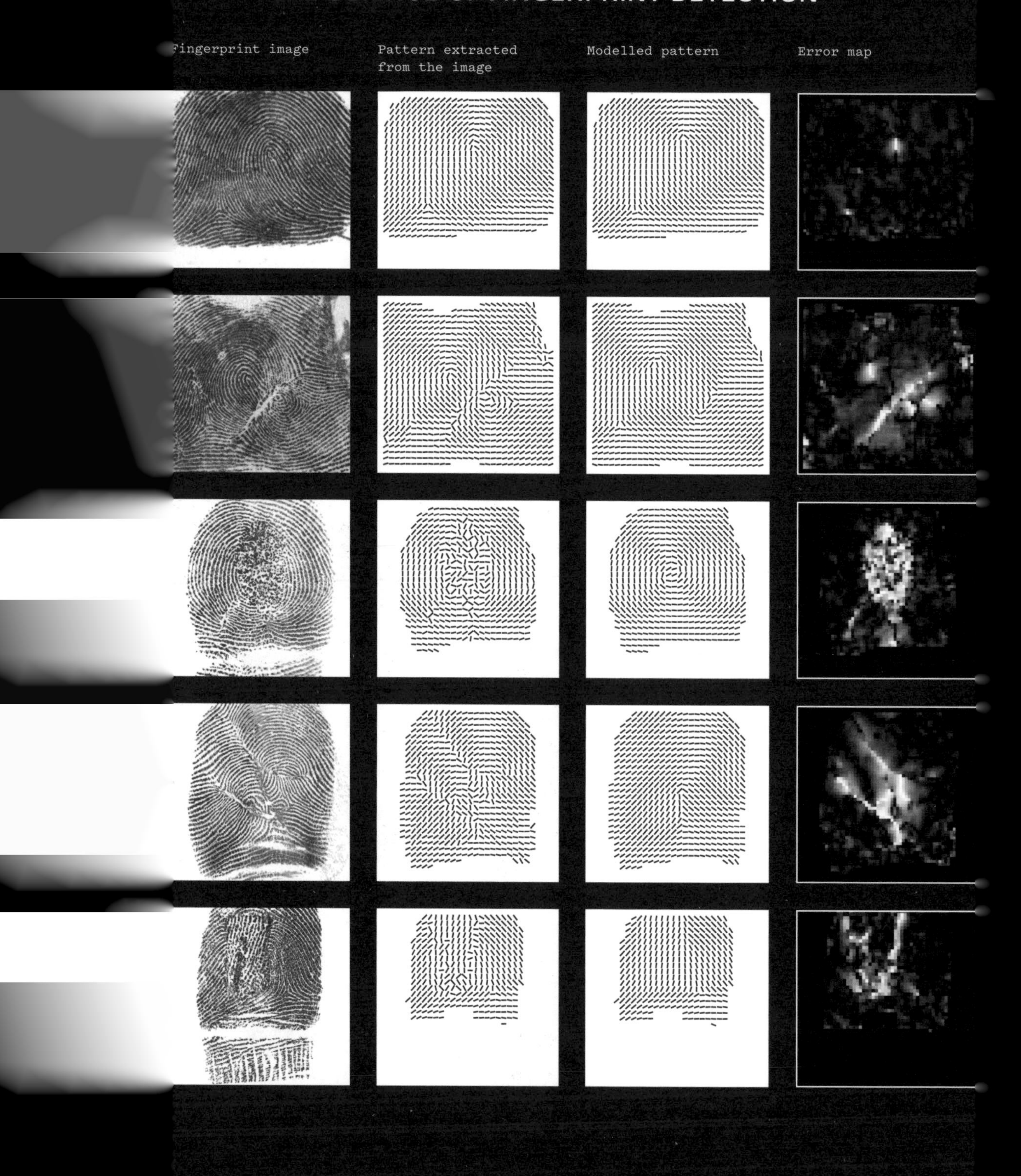

computer scientists at Michigan State University developed an algorithm to detect altered fingerprints
aring digitized versions of their patterns against computer-generated models of what the prints would
without tampering. This produces an error map that points to abnormalities: The more bright spots
likely a fingerprint has been distorted. A sample set of original prints is shown in the left column of the
m top to bottom, compare a natural, unaltered fingerprint to ones that are scarred, mutilated, distorted
-shaped incision, and obscured with a skin transplant. (Courtesy of "Altered Fingerprints: Analysis and
n," by S Yoon, J Feng, and AK Jain in the March 2012 edition of *IEEE Transactions on Pattern Analysis and*

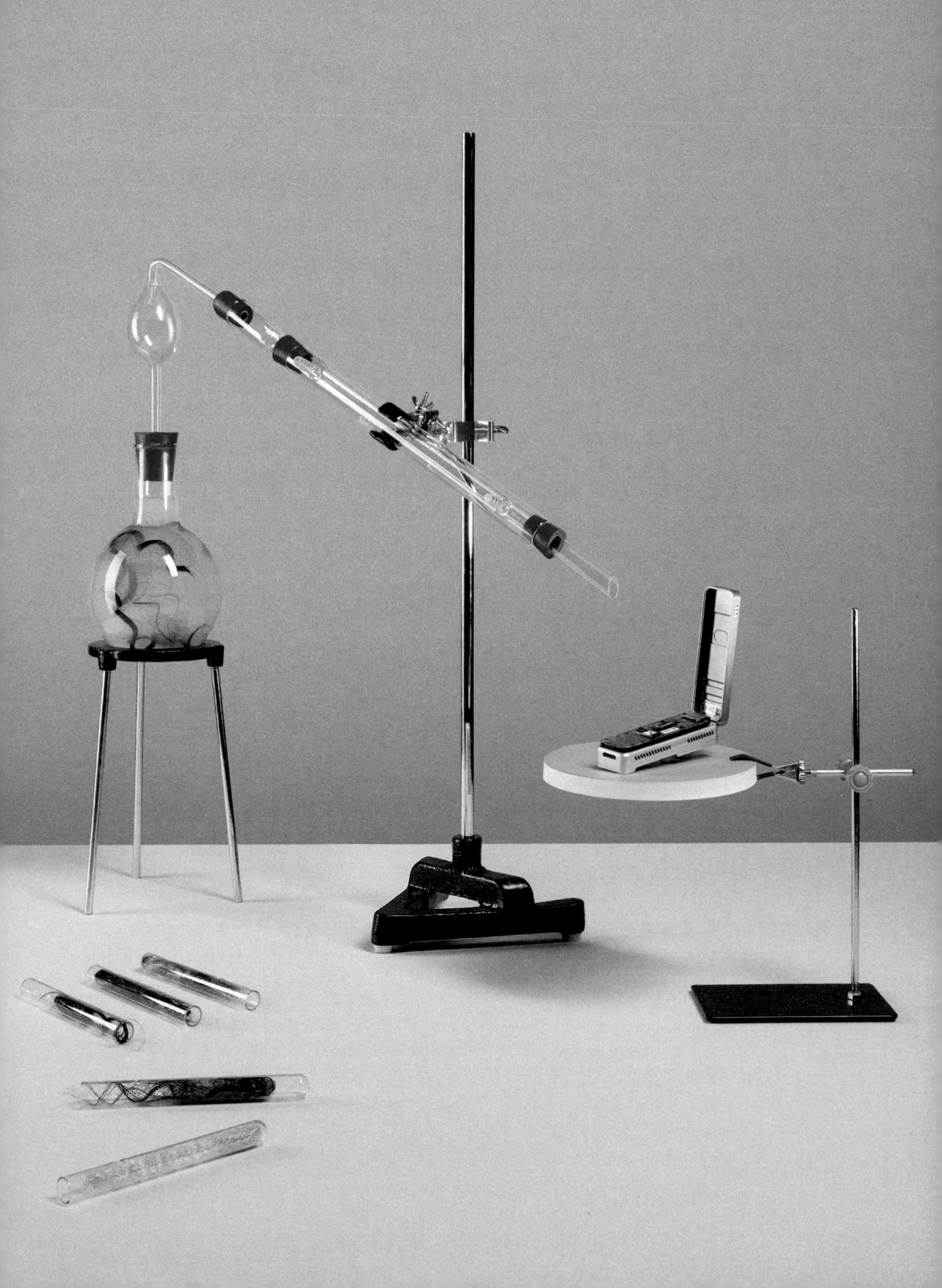

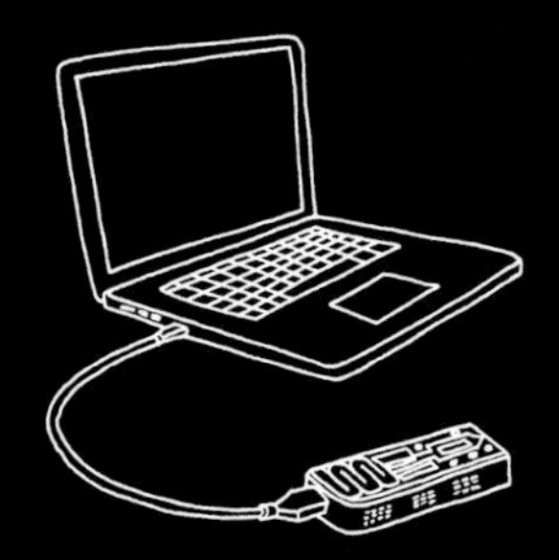

GENE-SEQUENCING MACHINE

Unraveling the code behind all living things

Most revolutions start small—but not the genetic revolution. The 13-year effort that kicked it off, the Human Genome Project, began in 1990 and still holds the record for the largest collaborative biology project.

At the heart of it was the humble gene-sequencing machine doing the important work of determining the order of four letters (A, T, G, and C) that make up genetic code. It cost about $3 billion to read the 3 billion letters that make up a single human genome for the first time. Less than 30 years later, sequencing a genome costs less than $1,000.

Gene sequencing has changed biology. Scientists use it in everything from detecting how epidemics spread to modifying human embryos. It has made possible tools that have transformed our lives, from genetically modified foods that feed billions to GM animals that help us find and test new treatments for human diseases. What comes in the future, from precision medicine to genetic cures, will be no less transformative.

Anything that pervades society so thoroughly raises thorny questions: Do we want a future with designer babies? Do we have the right to create changes that will be inherited by all future generations? It also raises worrying business questions: Who owns your genes? Who can afford enhancements and treatments? Is concentrating such powerful technologies in the hands of a few corporations worth it?

Many of these questions are already old, and some may never have a definitive answer. But that won't stop us from trying to influence our genetic destinies. The tireless gene-sequencing machine, which has gone from the size of a small room to the size of a large USB stick, is central to this progress.

↑ Oxford Nanopore MinIon gene-sequencing machine with test tubes. (Mathery)

IN 2016, A BOY WAS BORN WITH DNA FROM THREE PARENTS

In April 2016, a Jordanian woman gave birth in a hospital in Mexico. Her birth was normal in every way except one: The baby's genetic code was made from the DNA of three parents.

The novel birth was set in motion when the mother discovered that she carried defective mitochondria, which are the powerhouses inside every cell that break down nutrients into energy-rich molecules. Two of her children had previously died because this mitochondrial defect is passed down from mother to child. To fix the defect, John Zhang of the New Hope Fertility Center in New York found a donor (a third parent, in effect) to give her healthy mitochondria—and along with them 37 of the 20,000 genes that make up the human DNA of her son.

Humans have spent years debating whether we should apply our highly developed genetic tools[10] to altering humans, but Zhang made the leap. This follows years of work by ethicists and biologists in the UK, who in 2015 succeeded in making the three-parent procedure legal through an act passed in the British parliament.

Such bold experiments have allowed others to apply the procedure to fixing other kinds of human defects. In January 2017, a Ukrainian doctor used a similar technique on a second three-parent child. The technique was used for treating "embryo arrest" infertility, which occurs in one in 150 women and can't be fixed using conventional in-vitro fertilization techniques. Still, most scientists don't think the technique should be used for this treatment before more studies are conducted to verify its safety.

Zhang showed the world that we now have the tools and technology to genetically alter humans to create life. He says the rules are lax in Mexico compared to the UK, where the licenses to the three-parent baby procedure are tightly controlled. Some argue that such rogue uses of technology will lead us down a slippery slope. These critics fear that it will bring us closer toward eugenics by using new techniques such as CRISPR to edit out traits parents deem "undesirable."[11]

What we can achieve now is limited to tiny tweaks to the genetic code. This can help us target some highly specific genetic diseases, but we still don't know what 98.8% of the 3 billion letters of human DNA really do. In other words, we're nowhere near close to modifying DNA in a way that would allow us to edit out undesirable traits or endow desirable ones such as intelligence or height, which are controlled by hundreds of genes. Instead, in the coming decades, we are likely to see more treatments for the hundreds of single-gene diseases—an opportunity that scientists can't ignore.

↑ Studying the human genome at the Engelhardt Institute of Molecular Biology in Moscow. (Argonne National Laboratory/Getty)

[10]
Humans began genetically modifying organisms about 32,000 years ago when our ancestors chose to selectively breed the most docile wolves to become our cherished, trainable dogs. Later, selective breeding was used to alter corn, wheat, and other plants.

[11]
In 2015, Chinese researchers reported that they had successfully genetically modified human embryos using CRISPR technology. This shocked Western scientists, who have generally decided that modifying embryos is unethical, not to mention still risky.

WHAT SCIENTISTS SEE IN THE HUMAN GENOME

The human genome was first fully sequenced in 2003. Since then, the focus on genetic medical science has been identifying which genes—sequences of DNA that confer some inherited trait—trigger or raise the risk for disease. There are over 3 billion known DNA base pairs (ATCG: adenine with thymine, and cytosine with guanine), that together make up the complete instruction manual for your individual existence. Across 22 pairs of chromosomes (plus the X and Y sex chromosome, not shown here), scientists have already identified over 7,000 different genes that are connected to inherited traits. But there's still a lot left to learn about the human genome. Much of the space that appears empty here—the colored dots without any black—is actually filled with DNA. But we don't yet know what it all does. As scientists gather more genetic data from around the world, they'll start to identify additional markers for illness. As more precise genetic editing and manipulation techniques spread to labs internationally, the next few decades will almost certainly bring about a sea change in the way we diagnose and treat inherited illnesses.

A LOOK INSIDE CHROMOSOME 11

This small dot represents just one gene: OCA1A, which, when altered, causes a rare type of albinism. The disease is recessive. Every person has two copies of chromosome 11 (as they do all chromosomes) and two copies of OCA1A. If both your copies are mutated, then you'll have albinism.

The lines running through the circles represent a distinctive pattern of bands created when chromosomes are stained with certain chemicals in the lab. These are used by genetic scientists to locate specific genes. You can think of each as a sort of unique zip code within each chromosome.

Many people have heard of the BRCA1 and BRCA2 genes. Less-known is that if you are a carrier of a mutated ATM gene on chromosome 11—meaning at least one of your two ATM genes has the defect—you have just as high a risk for breast cancer as a mutated BRCA1 carrier.

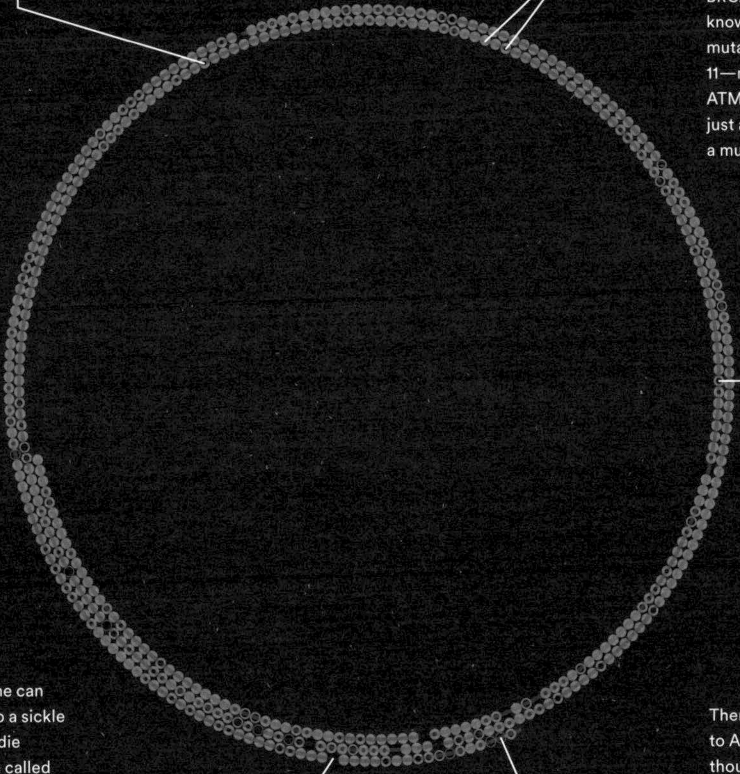

Mutations on the HBB gene can distort red blood cells into a sickle shape and cause them to die prematurely—a condition called sickle-cell anemia. In March 2017, doctors genetically altered the the bone marrow of a French teenager to compensate for his HBB gene defect, effectively curing his sickle-cell anemia.

There are a number of genes linked to ADHD, which we originally thought was purely behavioral. One of the most well-studied is DRD4, on chromosome 11, responsible for creating one of the five types of dopamine receptors in the human brain.

Chromosomes

1 6 11 16 21
2 7 12 17 22
3 8 13 18
4 9 14 19
5 10 15 20

Each colored dot represents a length of DNA code 13 kB, or 13,000 DNA base pairs, long. Chromosome 11 spans about 135 million base pairs; it comprises about 4% of the entire human genome. Number 11 is one of the most gene-rich—and disease-rich—chromosomes in the human genome. The black dots indicate regions on the human genome that scientists have identified as playing a role in some inherited trait; the majority are connected to disease or other health risks. Larger dots indicate many known genes in that region. (Data: Online Mendelian Inheritance in Man)

JUST BECAUSE YOUR DNA IS UNIQUE DOESN'T MEAN YOU OWN IT

The enormous scientific potential from the mapping of the human geonome also comes with enormous profit potential. It should come as no surprise then that fierce legal battles have been running alongside these scientific advances to establish both who owns your genetic data—no, it's not necessarily you—and who owns the technology that can exploit that data.

Meanwhile, consumer-facing companies offering cheap DNA analyses are building huge databases of genetic data—and handing them over to drug companies. 23andMe, for example, now has multimillion-dollar agreements to share customers' genetic data with drugmakers like Pfizer and is working with Genentech to start developing actual drugs, possibly for neurodegenerative diseases like Alzheimer's.

That means drug companies are the primary stewards of the world's biggest databases of human genomes. As the databases continue to grow, those who own the data will be the first to isolate key stretches of DNA connected to specific conditions. They will also get first crack at developing lucrative new tests and treatments based on those discoveries.

↑ Article 401 of Ecuador's 2008 constitution declares the country "free of GM seeds and crops, only by way of exception and in case of national interest." In Ecuador, 1,500 products—including Juicy Fruit gum—are sold with a warning that they contain genetically engineered ingredients. (May 2017. Johnny Simon for Quartz)

The most promising treatments will come through genetic-modification science, most likely CRISPR-Cas9 gene-editing technology. This too is the object of fierce legal battles, with billion-dollar biotech companies aligning with one side or another in the fight to prove ownership. When the dust settles, companies such as Novartis, Dupont, Monsanto, and GE Healthcare will drive—and profit from—the next stage of genetic science.

It's not necessarily bad that corporations will shape the future of gene-based science and medicine. After all, they employ some of the world's foremost researchers and fund some of the best-equipped research labs in the world. They also have the wherewithal—and profit incentive—to scale discoveries to levels where they can have a real impact on public health.

But handing over the genetic keys to corporations could mean genetics-based medicine isn't distributed equitably—it could be used to heal the wealthy and line the pockets of CEOs and shareholders. Some see a non-profit public repository of DNA as the solution. It's nice in theory, but it won't work, because de-identifying DNA is impossible.

The solution, ultimately, will not be sexy: It will be a complex negotiation of private-industry interest, non-profit advocacy, and government protection of individual rights.

Historical Correction

For the history of genetic sequencing to be adequately told, it must begin with a correction. The discovery of DNA is too often attributed to James Watson, Francis Crick, and Maurice Wilkins, who shared the 1962 Nobel prize for their discovery of the double-helix structure. At the time, the New York Times called it the "universal code for the perpetuation of each living thing in its image." But it would take years for the Times and others to add a key figure to DNA's backstory: Rosalind Franklin.

As a scientist at King's College London, Franklin produced an X-ray diffraction of DNA titled Photo 51, which crystallography experts called "the most beautiful X-ray photograph of any substance ever taken." She had applied her own painstaking mathematical calculations to the image to try to determine the three-dimensional form of DNA when Wilkins, who was a colleague of Franklin's, showed Photo 51 to Crick and Watson without her knowledge. The photograph ultimately allowed the duo to develop the double-helix theory of DNA. Franklin died of ovarian cancer at the age of 37 without knowing that Photo 51 had been part of Watson and Crick's discovery.

THIS SALMON IS THE FIRST GENETICALLY MODIFIED ANIMAL APPROVED TO EAT IN THE US

In 1995, AquaBounty Technologies applied to the US Food and Drug Administration for approval of a salmon that had been genetically modified to grow twice as fast and eat less than regular farmed salmon. In 2015, the FDA finally declared AquAdvantage safe for humans to eat. Nevertheless, a US law bans commercial sale of the fish until rules for how to label biotech animal products are finalized. If AquAdvantage's 20-year wait for FDA approval is any indication, that process could take years. (This photo shows two 22-month-old Atlantic salmon at the AquAdvantage facility in Prince Edward Island, Canada. The fish on the right has been genetically modified. March 2016, Greg Girard)

FOUR ANIMALS THAT COULD BE BROUGHT BACK FROM EXTINCTION

Thylacine—This marsupial, native to Australia and New Guinea, was a relative of kangaroos but looked more like a wolf. Humans hunted it to extinction by the 1930s; the last living animal died in captivity in 1936. In 2008, Dr. Andrew Pask, a researcher at the University of Melbourne, published a paper detailing how his team extracted DNA from a preserved thylacine and injected a portion of the Col2a1 gene, which regulates bone development, into mouse embryos, which grew normally. This was the first time DNA from an extinct animal performed its intended function in a living animal. This experiment has renewed scientists' hopes of eventually restoring the thylacine from extinction(Circa 1930, Popperfoto/Getty)

Gastric-brooding frog—This frog went extinct in the mid 1980s, likely due to pollution and disease. Native to Australia, the frogs are known for their unique reproduction method: The mother would convert her stomach into a womb, swallow her eggs, refrain from eating during the six-week gestation period, and give birth through "propulsive vomiting." In 2013, scientists at the University of New South Wales and the University of Newcastle tried to clone the frog by implanting a cell nucleus from a dead gastric-brooding frog into a live egg from another frog species. Professor Mike Archer hopes to continue using this method to make an embryo that will survive to the tadpole stage. (Feb. 1979, courtesy of Michael J. Tyler/University of Adelaide/Science Source)

Quagga—It's thought that the quagga became extinct due to overhunting in 1883, but in 1984, genealogy technology revealed that the quagga was a subspecies of the plains zebra, meaning it has the same DNA. The two species share the same genotype, though their phenotype, or observable characteristics, is different. The Quagga Project was started to try to recreate the quagga through artificial selection of plains zebras. The first quagga-like zebra foal was born in January 2005, and a fifth-generation foal was born in December 2013. Scientists hope continued selective breeding will lead to generations of plains zebras almost identical to the extinct quagga, which could then be released in the wild. (Circa 1930. Mansell/LIFE/Getty)

Heath hen—These birds were extremely common in northeastern US and were likely eaten at the Pilgrims' first Thanksgiving dinner in 1621. They were aggressively hunted for food over the next 300 years, and despite local conservation efforts, the last heath hens died in 1932. The wide availability of usable DNA from museum specimens makes the heath hen a de-extinction candidate. A conservancy group founded by Stewart Brand and Ryan Phelan is interested in restoring the bird through genetic technology. "The heath hen could well be the gateway bird to being able to bring genetic rescue to a wide variety of endangered and possibly extinct birds," Brand said in 2016. (Circa 1930, courtesy of the Vineyard Gazette)

De-extinction, which is the process of creating an organism that is a member of or closely resembles an extinct species, is a scientific process made possible through the use of gene-editing technology like cloning or selective breeding. While some scientists question the evolutionary benefits and point out that de-extinction resources could be better spent conserving existing species, the idea is popular in biotech and conservation communities. Here are four animals being considered as potential candidates for de-extinction.

ONE WAY TO FEED 1.8 BILLION INDIANS BY 2050

There's a food crisis looming in India, where farmers currently lose billions of dollars' worth of crops every year to pests and diseases. Droughts, coupled with inadequate irrigation systems, are exacerbating the problem. The average Indian already consumes a daily calorie amount that falls below the official poverty line, and the country's population is projected to grow by another 20% to over 1.5 billion by 2030.

Science has a solution to at least part of that problem: crops that are genetically modified to withstand pests and droughts.[12]

The most promising of these is a hybrid mustard plant, developed by a team of scientists from Delhi University. The GM plant, which yields 25% to 30% more than the original seed, is used to make one of the most popular edible oils in India. Its introduction promises to expand supply, lower cost, and reduce dependence on imports. (In 2014-15, India spent $10 billion importing 14.5 million metric tons of edible oils.)

But the Indian government is dragging its feet on approving the new seed for commercial use, placing it on seemingly perpetual hold. The reasons why are emblematic of people's conflicted relationship with GM products the world over.[13]

Mustard plants aren't India's first encounter with genetic modification. In 2002, the country approved the use of Bt cotton, which had been modified to resist pests like the bollworm. Its introduction was so wildly successful that it helped make India the second largest cotton manufacturer in the world.

Then, in 2015, disaster struck. GM plants in the cotton heartlands of India's northern states of Punjab and Haryana were lost to devastating attacks by the whitefly pest. The financial losses were massive.[14] Farmer suicides spiked in those regions.

The episode sowed deep mistrust of GM foods in India and heightened suspicion of government regulators. The hybrid mustard seed has stepped into this vortex.

Even if it survives the legal challenges against it and wins eventual government approval, public opinion may make the seed dead on arrival. Rakesh Tikait, a spokesperson for a leading farmers' organization in northern India, told Nature in January 2017 that his group will do all it can to keep the seed from getting planted. "If any shopkeeper is found selling GM mustard seed, all the seeds of his shop will be taken out and burnt and the shop's shutters welded," he said.

"Wherever anything lives, there is, open somewhere, a register in which time is being inscribed."—Henri Bergson

VINEYARD GAZETTE

Dr. Gross Announces Bird's Evident End In Official Report

"I AM THE LAST OF MY RACE. MY NAME ENDS WITH ME."

LAST HEATH HEN IS DEAD AND RACE IS NOW EXTINCT, EXPERT OBSERVERS AGREE

1 SURVIVOR SINCE 1929

COAST GUARD AIDS EFFORTS TO TRACE POLLUTION BY OIL

PLACE AND MANNER OF DEATH UNKNOWN

REPLETE WITH FOOD IN FLOODED PONDS, TROUT REJECT HOOKS

↑ The front page of the April 21, 1933 edition of the Vineyard Gazette, announcing that the heath hen was extinct. (Courtesy of the Vineyard Gazette)

[12] The most common biotech crops are cotton, soybeans, canola, and corn. The US is unique in producing GM sugar beets; China grows GM poplar trees; and Bangladesh is the only country farming GM eggplants.

[13] In 64 countries, food products are subject to "consumer right-to-know" laws, which require producers to label any food containing genetically modified ingredients. This is true in Australia, Japan, and all of the EU but not in Canada or the US.

[14] The Cavendish banana was planted decades ago as a monoculture crop in several countries and is now essentially the only banana sold in Western countries, with over 55 million metric tons produced annually. It is at risk of extinction due to seemingly unstoppable fungal disease.

A SELECTION OF GENETICALLY MODIFIED ANIMALS THAT GLOW, FEED, AND HEAL

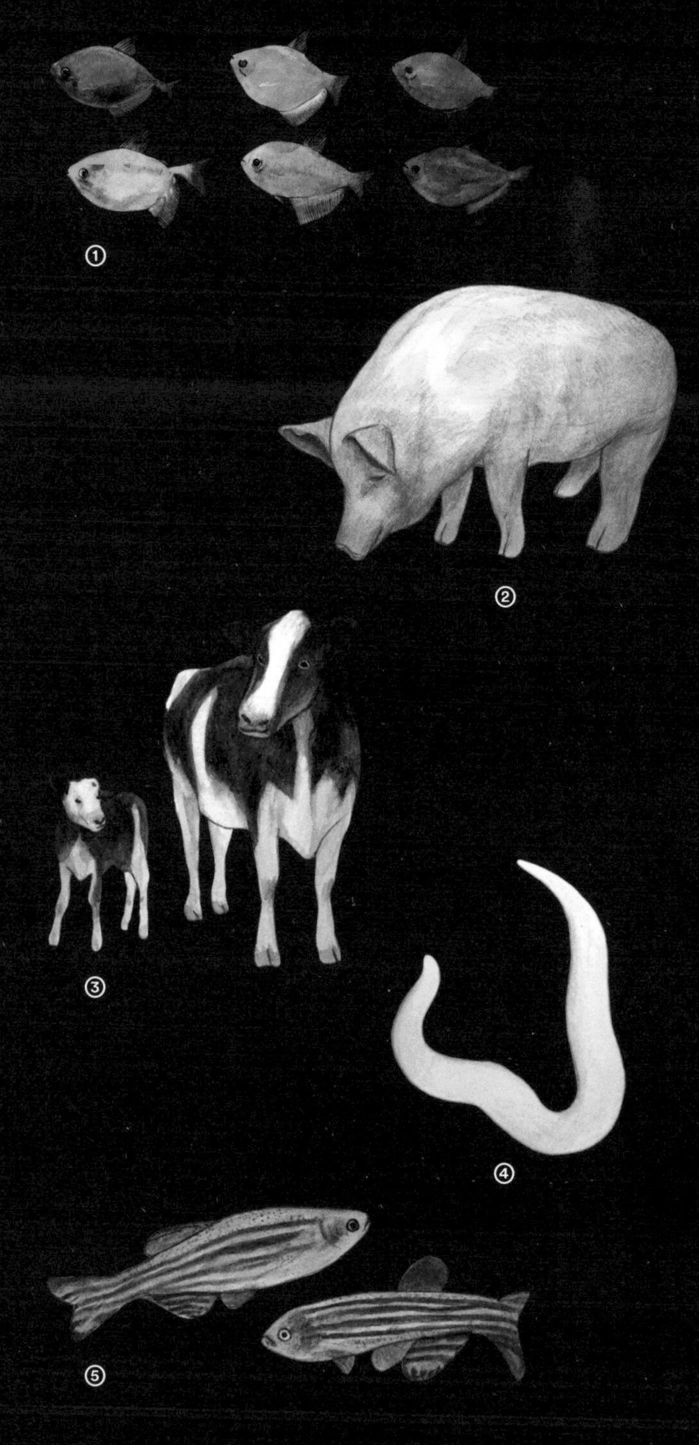

① GloFish, Yorktown Technologies, 2003. A Texas-based company developed GloFish, which glow in the dark thanks to sea-anemone genes.

② Muscular pigs, Seoul National University, 2012. Scientists mutated the MSTN gene that regulates muscle growth in these pigs, allowing their haunches to grow much bigger than they would naturally.

③ Hornless dairy cows, Recombinetics, 2016. Dairy cows have been modified to be naturally hornless so farmers don't have to dehorn them before they are shipped across the country.

④ Worms, University of Cambridge, 2016. Researchers genetically modified nematode worms to have Alzheimer's-like symptoms in order to successfully test a promising new treatment.

⑤ Glow zebrafish, University of Exeter, 2012. By inserting a fluorescent gene into zebrafish, scientists can show when the water they swim in has been polluted with environmental estrogens, like BPA.

⑥ Lyme-resistant mice, MIT Media Lab, 2017. Scientists are working to modify white-footed mice to be resistant to Lyme disease in order to prevent transmissions of tick-borne illnesses.

THE POWER OF THE MILLISECOND

On the morning of October 11, 1871, embers smoldered, looters picked over burnt-out storefronts, and newly homeless residents wandered the streets, clad in velvet robes and jewels, having saved only their most expensive belongings as they fled the flames. When a cow's tail caught the edge of a lantern nights before, it took only a millisecond for a spark to ignite the dry farm grass and set the blaze on its destructive path. In the ashes of the Great Chicago Fire, a city contemplated how to rebuild. And two architects saw a huge opportunity.

At the time of the fire, it was widely understood that skyscrapers were only possible in cities such as New York, where bedrock lies just below the surface. Nineteenth-century architects designed tall buildings that relied on this bedrock to support immense height and weight.

But after the fire, architects flocked to Chicago, eager to realize their visions on the suddenly empty swath of downtown real estate. Among them were Daniel Burnham and John Root. Though they were both just draftsmen when they met in 1872, they shared an aspiration to create "big buildings for big business."

One key challenge blocked their way: Chicago's soft clay soil.

They searched for a workaround—an innovation that would allow them to make the designs in their heads a possibility on the ground. They pioneered a solution beneath their Rookery project, an eleven-story building in the heart of Chicago's burgeoning Financial District. Using a grid of iron rails and beams encased in concrete, Burnham and Root invented a new "floating" foundation capable of supporting an enormous building's weight.

And, to top it off, the building included an elevator and electric lighting. The duo's innovations below the earth's surface—in the building's foundation—gave the Rookery the scale that allowed the architects to incorporate the newest aboveground inventions.

In the quarter century that followed, Chicago accelerated. Skyscrapers were erected, industry prospered, populations migrated. By 1893, the city had surpassed pre-fire expectations, even constructing an expanse of gleaming buildings to host the World's Fair (and its 27.5 million tourists). The city was reborn, and with it the entire practice of architecture.

A century later, seven people gathered in a San Diego home to challenge another industry stalled by tradition. These colleagues and friends schemed in the den, eventually reaching a shared vision: to leverage wireless technology to transform the quality and speed of communication. When they landed their first contract and set up shop in nearby La Jolla, their "quality communications" company—Qualcomm—was born.

At the time, the telecommunications industry was just beginning to integrate digital technologies but had a limited conception of what was possible. They were limited by technological constraints as insurmountable as the need for bedrock had once seemed to nineteenth-century architects. But, much like Burnham and Root, these seven individuals saw beyond presumed givens, imagining a new kind of foundation for the future of digital communication.

The newly formed Qualcomm had a vision of completely redefining the telecom industry: their inventions would serve as bedrock upon which to build tools that would accelerate information, accelerate interactions, and accelerate connectivity. For decades to come, this foundation would pave the way for information innovation to grow. Ultimately, these inventions would enable a future in which information can be shared by humans and their devices in a mere millisecond, 400 times faster than the blink of an eye.

Qualcomm plays a unique role as a "below the line" inventor for the industry, meaning that the company develops foundational technologies that form the bedrock for mobile communication. It is upon this strong foundation that vertical innovation—from products to businesses to entire new industries—can be built. Each icon represents an example of vertical innovation enabled by Qualcomm technology, from early pivots in 2G to the 5G future.

devices. This 360-degree awareness will go far beyond human line of sight, helping people drive more safely and bringing the autonomous vehicle a step closer to widespread implementation.

AR telemedicine and autonomous vehicles will rely on low latency for real-time response, but they are only the tip of the hyper-connected iceberg. The 5G framework is expected to scale data rates and power to provide extremely lean, low-cost connectivity for a growing ecosystem of connected devices. Instant access to information gathered by billions of intelligent connected sensors will unlock new efficiencies in the way we do everything from treating disease to growing food.

Imagine a power grid that never goes down because each node can repair itself or communicate with others to balance power loads. Imagine farmers being able to grow bumper crops year after year, no matter the weather, because low-power sensors in their fields give real-time data about soil health. New digital tools paired with more efficient use of resources will unlock earning potential for companies across sectors, boosting global output by as much as $12 trillion by 2035.

With increased efficiency, speed, and connectivity, 5G will be the tipping point from which we can scale the connected digital ecosystem to solve urgent problems. Latency has nearly been reduced to one millisecond, and with the entire tech industry poised to build 5G further, the power of that millisecond is seemingly limitless.

Over a hundred years ago, Burnham and Root laid the foundation for a city of skyscrapers, but never could have imagined the networks that would eventually connect today's Rookery with the world around it.

Twenty years ago, employees in that same building looked forward to sending email on their phones but could never have predicted ridesharing or AR telemedicine.

Today, we can envision a world of autonomous vehicles, VR, and smart sensors, where a single millisecond stands between us and a world of possibility. It's impossible to predict what new heights will be reached from this 5G foundation. But if history is any indication, by tomorrow's major breakthrough Qualcomm will already be at work on the next paradigm shift in the way we connect, the way we work, and the way we live.

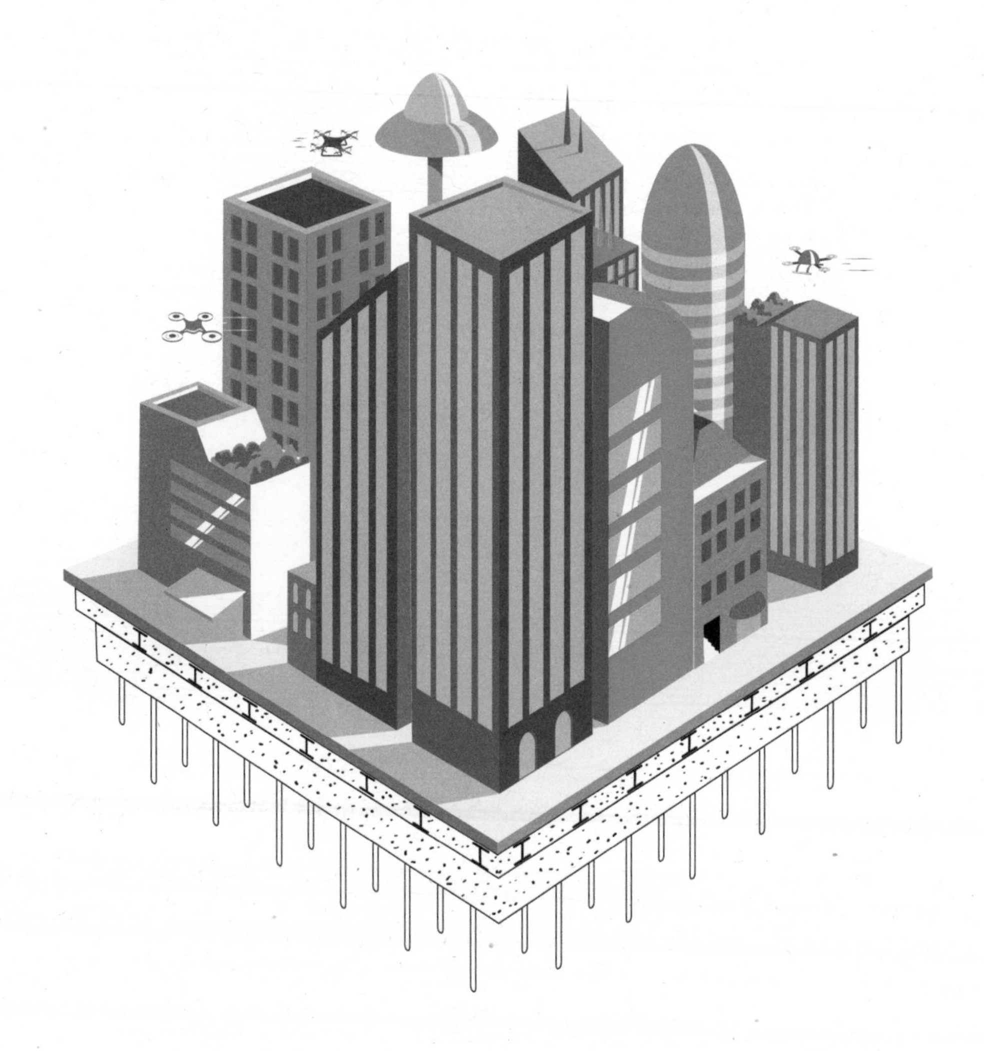

This chapter was produced on behalf of Qualcomm by Quartz Creative and not by the Quartz editorial staff.

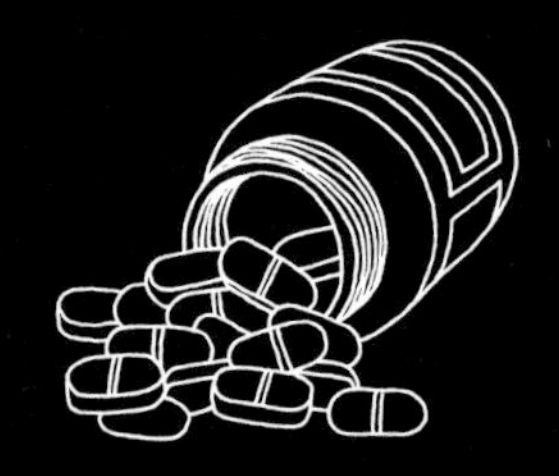

MODAFINIL

Modifying the mind for a more productive life

If the Olympic motto is "Faster, Higher, Stronger," then the modern workplace motto is "Smarter, Faster, Better." To excel in today's global economy, you need more brain than brawn.

For a large section of the working population, interventions that make us smarter—prenatal care, early-childhood nutrition, better education, and thicker wallets—are advantages we take for granted. But there are new shortcuts available. Cognitive enhancers are now being consumed by C-suite executives, schoolchildren, college students, young entrepreneurs, and aging office workers.

Humans have always sought an extra mental edge, from a simple coffee on the way to work to amphetamines in the battlefield. But smart pharmaceuticals may bestow more than simple energy and focus. Modafinil, originally developed to treat sleep disturbances like narcolepsy and sleep apnea, has been shown to enhance attention, improve learning, and boost our ability to solve problems and think creatively. Known as the first "true smart drug" by pharmacologists, modafinil has become popular as a brain hack in part because it's thought to have fewer side effects than traditional stimulants.

Researchers and entrepreneurs are both still learning about how the mind and brain work: Electric brain stimulation may be the next big thing in treating depression; over-the-counter supplements called nootropics are popular in Silicon Valley; and even placebo pills work for some. Whether such enhancements are ethical or desirable will continue to be debated for as long as humans have bodies, but most people aren't waiting for academics to offer approval. When a colleague has found a way to get ahead, it's all too tempting to follow suit.

↑ Still life with coffee, toast and jam, and modafinil. (Mathery)

AN OXFORD PHILOSOPHER ON HOW IT FEELS TO TAKE MODAFINIL

One in five academics surveyed by the journal Nature in 2008 admitted to using cognitive enhancers. Anders Sandberg, a philosopher at the Future of Humanity Institute at Oxford University, is among them. We asked him about his modafinil use:

Where do you get your supply of modafinil?

I order it online. I get my chemist friend to test it for purity.

What dosage do you use?

I use 100 milligrams. I've been arguing with a modafinil researcher who suggests using 200 mg, which is the dosage commonly used in studies. I don't see a particular benefit with a higher dosage, but it may be because my body metabolizes the drug more slowly than average.

That raises another problem: The drug's effects depend on individual biochemistry. I have a friend who suffers from narcolepsy and takes 800 mg of modafinil but still suffers from sleep episodes. I once went to an academic conference where everybody at my table had tried modafinil. When they described its effects, they were all over the place: One said that they became more social, one felt sharper, and one felt much more anxious.

When do you take modafinil and what's the effect?

I set my alarm 30 minutes before wake-up time. I take the pill when the alarm rings and then go back to sleep. In 30 minutes, I wake up full of energy. The effect lasts most of the day, and I have no problems sleeping.

There's a stimulating effect that's useful, but that's not the real benefit of modafinil. Getting stuff done is great, but you can do that with coffee.

Modafinil lowers my activation threshold: I'm more motivated to take on tasks I would normally put off. I can hold them in my mind better. So it doesn't really help me when I'm doing normal research, but when I'm listening to a philosopher or tackling a difficult problem, modafinil seems to help.

I probably use it once every two weeks. I like to space it out because if I take it for many days at a time, the effect wears off.

↑ In 1884, Burroughs Wellcome & Co began manufacturing pills that contained cocaine. The pills were available over the counter at Harrod's and legal until the 1920s. (Bottle from circa 1884, courtesy of Royal Pharmaceutical Society of Great Britain)

Go pills

In 2008, the JASON Defense Advisory Panel, an elite group of scientists, reported to the Pentagon that the best soldier was not the strongest or the fastest but the most well-rested. "If an opposing force had a significant sleep advantage, this would pose a serious threat," they wrote, adding that spy agencies should "monitor enemy activities in sleep research."

To conquer drowsiness, soldiers have turned to amphetamines for decades, though the drugs can cause anxiety and confusion; US pilots who killed four Canadian soldiers in a 2002 "friendly fire" incident in Afghanistan blamed "go pills" they took before the mission.

Now modafinil offers alertness without the negative side effects. In 2016, scientists from the Naval Medical Research Unit subjected soldiers to mental and physical exercises during a grueling 37-straight-hours awake. Those given modafinil performed better than those given caffeine gum.

The UK, France, and, reportedly, India have all used modafinil to keep their troops awake."Let's put it this way: If an adversary is using it, you simply can't afford not to," says Maxwell Mehlman, a professor of law and bioethics at Case Western Reserve University.

• Atta Boateng Jr., research assistant: "You feel much more focused on your tasks. It gives you more concentration, even afterward. You feel the effects for about five to 10 minutes."

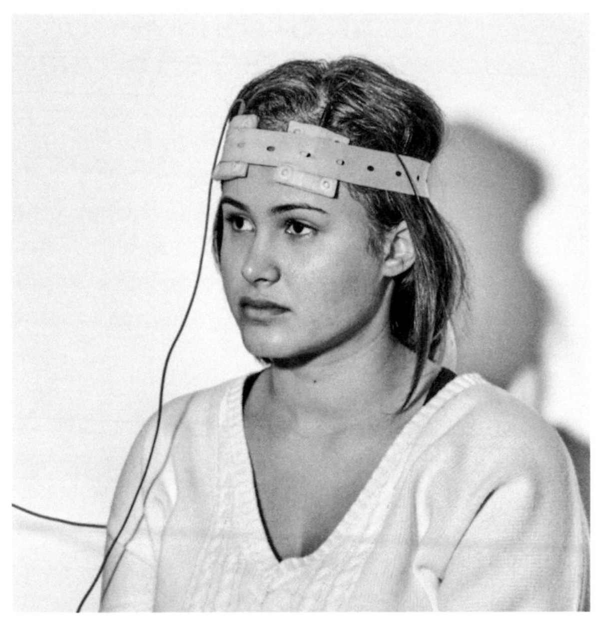

• Helen Borges, researcher: "My current research tests the tolerability of certain current intensities and other novel aspects of tDCS. Our findings could be used in both healthy populations and those experiencing cognitive deficit due to disorders."

• Libby Ho, undergraduate researcher: "I felt a prickly feeling, but it was interesting. We're working on testing tolerability and measuring how much people feel pain."

• Nigel Gebodh, research assistant: "I'm coupling electroencephalogram (EEG) and tDCS so that researchers can monitor the brain during stimulation and spot 'artifacts' like the blink of an eye."

ELECTRICAL BRAIN STIMULATION OFFERS THE NEXT GREAT HOPE FOR CURING WHAT AILS THE MIND

Rustin Berlow (right) believes electrical stimulation can cure what ails the brain. More specifically, he believes in transcranial direct-current stimulation (tDCS), which relies on a device powered by a nine-volt battery and delivers a current of up to two milliamps to the brain. Berlow, a psychiatrist with a private practice in Del Mar, California has seen remarkably fast, lasting responses to tDCS in patients whose depression had not responded to drugs or psychotherapy. In a typical session, Berlow places saline-soaked electrodes on his patient's head at different locations depending on the goal—over the motor cortex to improve athletic performance or the prefrontal cortex to relieve symptoms of depression. There's no conclusive medical evidence on whether the treatment works, but in early 2017, there were hundreds of open clinical trials testing its efficacy in mood and eating disorders, stroke recovery, dementia, and more. Meanwhile, tDCS has attracted thousands of DIY brain hackers and nerdy fringe groups who want to improve their chess game, pass an exam, or become better traders. Berlow is waiting for pop culture to make tDCS more mainstream: All it will take is one movie showing a character using it, he says, and "brain stimulation will capture the public's imagination." (Jan. 2017. Cait Oppermann for Quartz)

To date, most tDCS research has focused on the primary motor cortex, which is involved in motor control, by testing brain stimulation for stroke victims.
The sponges placed between the electrodes and the patient's skin are first soaked in saline to improve conductivity and reduce the risk that a patient will feel any burning.
The electric current, up to two milliamps, can only enhance existing neural activity, not spark new connections.

Adderall for all

University of Richmond philosopher Jessica Flanigan believes cognitive enhancers have a place in the classroom.

"People think further cognitive enhancements would be really bad, but they don't see all of the cognitive enhancements that we've already achieved: better education, prenatal care, early-childhood nutrition, and rising resources due to development. We wouldn't think that it was a mistake to cognitively enhance people in those ways.

"A risk-benefit calculus for prescribing stimulants shouldn't be limited only to children who have a clinical diagnosis of ADHD. It should be broadened to think about whenever the benefits would outweigh the risks, and we shouldn't limit ourselves to these narrow, medicalized criteria.

"There are other kinds of impairments that aren't ADHD. For example, having an open classroom or a very loud school. That's not a learning disability or cognitive impairment, but in some ways that's an environmental impairment that could merit prescribing stimulants to help kids focus.

"Obviously, the thing that should be done is education reform. But failing any kind of policy solution, I think that it would be a mistake to say, 'I guess there's nothing we can do!' We know that in some cases, academic outcomes can be achieved by just prescribing stimulants."

SHOPPING FOR ADDERALL ON THE DARK WEB

Adderall was first brought to market in the US in 1996 and quickly became the most popular drug to treat ADHD in children. Today, nearly half of the prescriptions are written for children, mostly boys between 12 and 18. But more young adults are now being treated: About 4.5% of Americans aged 18 to 25 have an Adderall prescription for ADHD.

Off-label use has grown exponentially in the last 20 years, in part from adults seeking sharper focus. The research is ambiguous on whether Adderall actually offers better focus if you don't have ADHD, but the black market for Adderall is growing regardless.

It is also developing new supply routes. Since the secondary-prescription market can only offer a limited supply of the drug, more users are turning to the dark web, which is a corner of the internet where online stores traffic in illicit and often illegal goods for sale in bitcoin. Here, the supply of Adderall appears unlimited.

Dozens of vendors advertise their goods with photos of small pink or orange pills. In most markets, more supply means lower prices, but this isn't the case on the dark web. For example, it costs about $20 for a 20 mg Adderall pill compared to just $5 on the street.

There's a good reason for the high price: Customers are paying a premium for a reliable supply.

Carnegie Mellon University computer scientist Nicolas Christin scraped data from the largest dark-web vendors. According to Christin, dark-web sales of Adderall more than tripled between 2013 and 2015 but still remain small: It accounts for less than 1% of dark-web drug sales, relative to cannabis and MDMA, which have exploded in popularity.

Many dark-web Adderall vendors claim they source their product from labs in India that manufacture generic versions of the pills. Product reviews serve an essential quality-control function (though it's less safe than government regulation). Without good reviews, it's nearly impossible to sell your product. Unreviewed vendors must therefore offer special deals; one on AlphaBay Market advertises "Free 20mg Adderall" and says in its listing, "Getting a good rating is hard to do so we are giving away 1 20mg IR (instant release) to the first 40 people who buy. We will only ship one if you order multiple units."

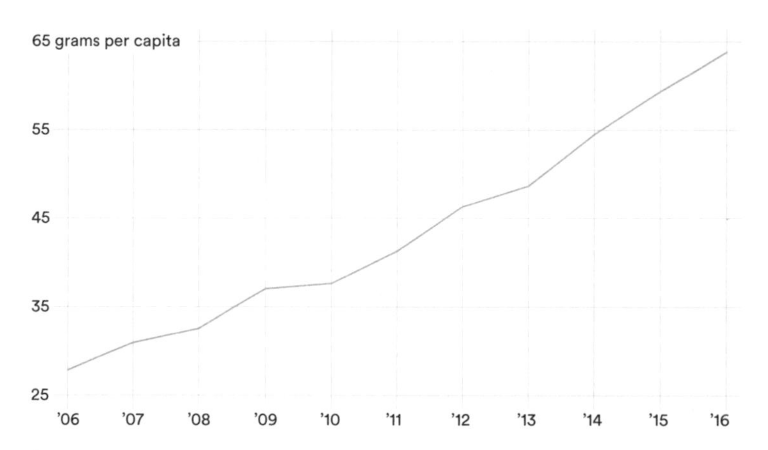

↑ US distribution of amphetamines to treat ADHD.
Data: Automated Reports and Consolidated Ordering System

LITTLE SHOP OF STIMULANTS

The convenience-store market in Asia is surging. There was a 44% increase in the number of such shops from 2012 to 2016, largely thanks to rapid urbanization and a growing young population. Traditional cafés are struggling to find retail space in crowded cities as real-estate prices skyrocket, but big international convenience chains like 7-Eleven and FamilyMart can afford the steeper rent. They're also expanding in-store offerings to keep up with consumer demand for coffee; the annual rise in coffee consumption in Asia between 2012 and 2016 was more than double the global average. To meet this need, convenience stores (like the one pictured above in Hong Kong) have started offering self-service coffee machines and café-style drinks for about the same price as instant coffee, the longtime coffee drink of choice in Asia. (March 6, 2017, Shek Po Kwan for Quartz)

IN KENYA, WOMEN RUN THE KHAT TRADE

Rose Mugambi Karanja remembers the morning she got into the khat business over 20 years ago. When she apprenticed for a khat trader, she learned how the green twigs were cultivated and picked and became familiar with how khat was wrapped and shipped. The demand for khat—a red-stemmed, green-leafed plant chewed for its amphetamine-like properties—was booming in the town of Maua, located in the Nyambene Hills in eastern Kenya.

"It really changed my life," Karanja recalls. Since then, she's profited enough from the khat industry to be able to invest in property and farms and send her children to school and university.[15] "I got in and never looked back," she says.

Women were among the first to discern how lucrative the khat business can be. In Maua, women pick leaves from the plants, collect and sell the banana leaves used to wrap khat in bundles, knit and prepare the sacks used to transport khat, and act as brokers between farmers and traders who export it.

Since the 1990s, khat has moved from a social product consumed in the Horn of Africa to a global commodity, boosted by improvements to infrastructure and transportation systems.

An estimated 500,000 Kenyans depend on khat for their livelihoods, with the UK importing some $25 million-worth of the leaves annually before a 2014 law banned imports of the plant. Still, more than 15 cargo planes full of khat leave Kenya for Somalia daily with a retail value of $400,000. Khat is also planted, traded, and chewed in Yemen, where the plant takes up 15% of the country's agricultural land. In Ethiopia, nearly half a million hectares (1,235,000 acres) is devoted to planting khat, with exports now accounting for the country's second-largest source of foreign currency.

Experts have debated the long-term withdrawal symptoms associated with khat and whether it induces psychosis. This has led to bans in countries like the UK, despite an official recommendation from the Home Office's Advisory Council on the Misuse of Drugs that khat remain legal. The loss of the British market, which consumed between 2,500 to 2,800 metric tons a year, has left many farmers and traders in Maua with huge losses.

"Since the London ban, some of the women we worked with have completely left the business," says Charity Gakongu, who wraps khat in banana leaves at the Muringeni market in Maua. "People don't know how to do anything else. Where do you want them to go?"

[15]
In 2017, Stanford neuroscientists used brain scans to conclude that an ancient method of memory training called the "method of loci," a.k.a. the "memory palace technique," was superior to drill-like exercises.

To use the method, first picture your childhood home or another well-known space or route. Next, mentally place the objects (words, numbers, or names) that need to be remembered in specific locations throughout that place or along that route. When you need to recall those objects, mentally stroll through the room again, looking around for the memories now mentally embedded there.

↑ Men chewing khat as they wait to vote in Sana'a, the capital of Yemen. (Sept. 1999, Rabih Moghrabi/AFP/Getty)

PLACEBO PILLS ARE GIVING SOME PEOPLE WHAT THEY REALLY WANT IN LIFE

In 2012, Robert Richman, a former manager at Zappos, started handing out Tic Tacs at Burning Man. He gave the cinnamon candies to dozens of friends and passersby saying, in jest, that the breath mints would awaken them to reality and let them achieve what they wanted—just as the red pill did for Neo in *The Matrix*.

Richman forgot about the stunt until weeks later, when people started telling him the pill was working.

They were now launching new businesses and quitting dead-end relationships. A psychologist who had taken the Tic Tacs made it part of her counseling practice; patients taking her placebo pills began reporting breakthroughs.

After a few years experimenting with friends, Richman officially launched Xpill in January 2017. For about $400, participants get a three-month supply of placebo pills (which are clearly labeled "Rice Powder" on the front), support from coaches and an online community, and instructions for a daily ritual: Express a deeply held intention, write it down, and take the pill.

Richman says Xpill's potency is in the mind, not the capsule. "I tell people there is nothing in the pill," he says. "Whether it's working or not is up to you."

It may sound impossible, but the efficacy of placebo pills has been known for decades. Researchers have recently turned their attention to so-called "open-label placebo" trials, in which patients know they are taking fake pills. Harvard Medical School professor Ted Kaptchuk reports these pills can relieve conditions defined by "self-observation" symptoms such as pain, nausea, or fatigue.[16] "People can still get a placebo response, even though they know they are on a placebo," Kaptchuk said in 2016. "You don't need deception or concealment for many conditions to get a significant and meaningful placebo effect."

Researchers who study biochemistry say these placebos work because our brains learn to connect experience with expectation. Tor Wager, a professor at the University of Colorado Boulder, has run experiments that conditioned participants to expect pain relief from a cream with no medicinal value. Once he applied the cream, people's brains would signal the nervous system to trigger their bodies' release of natural opioids, which created the pain-relief effect it was expecting.

The Xpill doesn't work for everyone, Richman says. But for some, the Xpill exposes what's really important. "People just start cutting stuff out of their lives they don't need anymore: relationships, old jobs, stuff they don't like anymore," he says. "It triggers something in your subconscious mind. Once you swallow a pill, you can't go back."

[16]
Scribonius Largus, a pharmacologist who lived in 1 AD, believed in electronic brain hacking. He used torpedoes (a type of electric ray fish) to treat headaches. This fish appeared in Greek and Arab medical texts but was viewed with superstition in the medieval era.

The paan economy

The fruit of the areca palm or betel nut is the fourth most used stimulant in the world after tobacco, alcohol, and caffeine.

It's most commonly consumed by placing limestone powder, crushed areca nut, fennel, and a paste made of catechu (an extract from the acacia tree) and water on the inside of a betel leaf, folding it into a small package, and then chewing it.

In India, this concoction is known as "paan" and is central to an informal retail economy. Streets across the country and rural areas are lined with tiny shops selling paan parcels. Over the last decade, these small shops, which are typically run by a single person known as the "paanwalla," have become mini retail establishments selling everything from cigarettes and chocolates to biscuits and chips.

Prakash Chandra Kashyap, a paan-shop owner in Thane, a suburb of Mumbai, says that a shop's earnings depend on the location. The 42-year-old makes 1,000 rupees ($15.50) a day. Paan is sold at a price range of anywhere between Rs10 to Rs200, but it can go higher if exotic ingredients like chocolate and Nutella are added. For those who don't consume paan with tobacco, it has become a post-dinner ritual that aids in digestion; the fancier versions sometimes even replace dessert.

BEYOND COFFEE: THE WORLD SPRAYS, DRINKS, AND CHEWS CAFFEINE, TOO

01.

01.
Chocolate contains theobromine, a stimulant chemically similar to caffeine. Milk chocolate contains 9 mg of caffeine and 64 mg of theobromine per 1.5 oz. (42 grams), and dark chocolate contains 20 mg of caffeine and 176 mg of theobromine per 1.5 oz. Above, a woman choosing from a box of chocolates. (Circa 1940, Keystone View/ FPG/Getty)

02.
Guarana is a fruit found in South America whose beans are 3.6% to 5.8% caffeine by weight. In the US it is used in energy shots and drinks.

03.
Energy drinks including VitaminWater (20 oz.), 5-Hour Energy (6 oz.), Monster (16 oz.), and Red Bull (16 oz.) contain between 50 mg to 230

04.
Diet pills like Hydroxycut contain up to 200 mg of caffeine per pill. There is no definitive research on whether increased caffeine intake suppresses your appetite.

05.
Over-the-counter pain relievers like Excedrin Extra Strength, Excedrin Migraine, and Midol contain 65 mg of caffeine, which can reduce pain perception in the brain to enhance the medicine's effects and reduce inflammation.

06.
Yerba mate, a South American beverage of steeped leaves from the *Ilex paraguariensis* tree, has about 80 mg of caffeine per serving. Here Paraguayan footballer Cristian Riveros drinks "tereré," a typical Paraguayan yerba mate infusion prepared with cold water. (June 21, 2010, Juan Mabromata/AFP/Getty)

06.

07.
Jolt gum contains roughly 50 mg of caffeine per piece.

08.
Caffeine powders are dehydrated forms of the stimulant that can be added to any food or drink. A serving contains between 50 mg and 200 mg of caffeine but should be used with caution. Lethal doses can be as low as 600 mg.

09.

09.
Sodas first used caffeinated kola nuts as part of cola. Soda makers noticed that consumers enjoyed the stimulant's effects and began including it in other sodas. The amount of caffeine per 12 oz. ranges from 18 mg (root beer) to 55 mg (Moutain Dew); a can of Coke has roughly 35 mg. Above, French chemist Albert Bonn analyzing the ingredients of Coca-Cola. (Mark Kauffman/LIFE /Getty)

Bitcoin: A Peer-to-
Electronic Cash System
Nakamoto
@gmx.com
www.bitcoin.org
Abstract. A purely
version of electronic cash would allow online

SATOSHI'S PAPER

Blockchain and the decentralization of power

One technology has increasingly perplexed economists, cryptographers, and entire governments since 2008: the cryptocurrency bitcoin and its animating principle, the blockchain.

The idea of bitcoin was set out in a PDF published on bitcoin.org in October 2008. The author, who went by the name Satoshi Nakamoto, announced it in a 255-word email to a mailing list for cryptography enthusiasts: "I've been working on a new electronic cash system that's fully peer-to-peer, with no trusted third party." It drew a handful of largely skeptical replies. But by January, Satoshi returned with an answer for his critics: a piece of software that put his paper in practice—bitcoin version 0.1.

Satoshi's scheme was a technological chimera, combining cryptography, the Austrian School of economics, and the internet's decentralized structure to produce a form of money that was controlled by no one but could be owned by anyone.

Traditional currencies rely on people trusting the issuer: If that trust is lost, the currency is worthless. Bitcoin requires no trust beyond the irrefutable logic of mathematics. It's transferred over a blockchain, which is a digital ledger spread over a global network of computers designed so that no one party can easily take control. As tamper-proof registries, blockchains can do more than transfer digital cash: They can be repositories for medical records, real-estate deeds, and financial data. They are also the foundation of successful new cryptocurrencies, like ethereum.

Governments are catching up. There's a growing recognition that digital money can better control a nation's money supply and its economy's stability. In an inversion of bitcoin's founding logic, the ideas Satoshi unleashed are now being co-opted by institutional powers.

↑ Satoshi's paper with brick and shattered glass. (Mathery)

WHEN CRYPTOCURRENCIES FEEL SAFER THAN COLD, HARD CASH

When governments assault the edifice of money by banning banknotes or by driving their economies over a cliff, citizens increasingly turn to bitcoin.

The stateless cryptocurrency was there for Cypriots in 2013 when a financial crash led to capital controls; the Greeks in 2015 as it looked like the country might tumble out of the euro zone; Venezuelans, who have seen their life savings eroded by triple-digit inflation; and Indians, who were left reeling after large-denomination banknotes were abruptly removed from circulation in 2016.

In each instance, the price of bitcoin surged as state-issued fiat currencies were rocked by uncertainty. Indeed, this inverse correlation between an ascendant cryptocurrency and troubled, state-backed money is the very point of bitcoin: a better, safer store of value for the networked world. Bitcoin's creator, the pseudonymous Satoshi Nakamoto,[17] made this clear by inscribing a headline from the Times of London in 2009 in the so-called "genesis block," which is the first chunk of bitcoin ever mined: "Chancellor on brink of second bailout for banks."

While bitcoin's critics have long pointed out that the cryptocurrency hasn't yet found its killer application—whether as a cheap payments system to rival Visa and Mastercard or a remittance channel that would kill off Western Union—price trends suggest that demand for the cryptocurrency spikes when faith in a government-backed currency falters.

This in turn suggests that bitcoin fulfills one of the three features of money: acting as a reliable store of value. Bitcoin hasn't quite got the other two nailed down yet—being a unit of account and a medium of exchange—but a legion of startups and, increasingly, established institutions are working on it.

Of course, it's not as if all Greeks or Venezuelans are exchanging their euros and bolivars for bitcoins. Purchasing the digital currency can still be tricky, and there's the persistent risk of being hacked or simply losing the private key to your wallet. What data are available on currency-exchange volumes is fragmented and can't be used to conclusively say that specific crises drove the price of bitcoin up at the time. But it's a reasonable hypothesis.

13th-century accounting

The merchants of medieval Tuscany wouldn't recognize today's companies, but they would be able to read their accounts (more or less). Double-entry bookkeeping dates at least back to Florentine firms in the 13th century. The Franciscan friar and mathematician Luca Pacioli, a frequent collaborator with Leonardo da Vinci, later codified the practices of the self-balancing system of recording debits and credits; texts based on his work were reproduced, translated, and distributed widely across Europe.

Accounting practices now reflect the complexity of modern business—Pacioli would have been flummoxed by the concepts of non-current deferred revenue or contingent tax assets—but the fundamental principles underlying corporate ledgers remain the same as they were back then.

↑ A cuneiform tablet from Mesopotamia shows a list of expenditures. (Circa 605-562 BC, courtesy of the Metropolitan Museum of Art)

[17]
Several attempts to identify Satoshi have been made, but none have been successful. In 2016, an Australian named Craig Wright claimed to be part of a group that operated under Satoshi Nakamoto's pseudonym, but he was unable to provide cryptographic proof to back up his assertion.

SINCE 2015, MORE THAN 90% OF BITCOIN EXCHANGES HAVE BEEN LINKED TO CHINA

[18]
A bitcoin startup called 21 is paying people in bitcoin to answer questions posed by paying customers about their jobs and work skills. Its CEO believes the bitcoin revolution is coming, but we need to begin earning bitcoin instead of buying and trading it for dollars.

No one in the world has taken a shine to cryptocurrency like the Chinese. Well over 90% of the volume on bitcoin exchanges since 2015 to early 2017 has either featured Chinese yuan or taken place on Chinese exchanges. There's a good reason for this enthusiasm.

The Chinese government makes it very hard for ordinary residents to exchange yuan for another currency and move it out of China. Forced to keep their money in the country, investors have limited options: the volatile stock market, frothy bond and housing markets, and dodgy non-bank investment products. None is very appealing. That's why enterprising Chinese daytraders have taken to playing the bitcoin market.

↑ Two views of a bitcoin mining facility in the mountains near Kongyuxiang, in China's Sichuan province, owned by HaoBTC. (Aug. 12, 2016, Paul Ratje/Washington Post/Getty)

Some aren't speculating, though—they're using bitcoin exchanges to circumvent government money-changing limits and swap their yuan for bitcoins, and those bitcoins for foreign currency.[18] This hits at the raison d'être of a cryptocurrency: underpinning an economy that operates beyond government reach.

Since mid 2014, slowing economic growth has spurred international investors to ditch their Chinese assets, which has pushed the yuan's value down—and compelled other countries to debase their own currencies in kind, fearful of becoming less competitive with the export-oriented powerhouse. All the while, the Chinese government, which tightly controls the yuan's value against a basket of currencies, has been making it even harder to exchange yuan for foreign money.

This is probably why every time the government lets the yuan's value drop, Chinese bitcoin trading surges. It's also likely why the cryptocurrency's price plummeted in early 2017 after the government launched a probe into bitcoin exchanges. The bitcoin market then rallied, regaining its value to pre-probe levels within a month or so.

WHEN TURMOIL STRIKES, BITCOIN SPIKES

March 17, 2013
Cypriot banks run low on cash

June 25, 2015
Lead-up to Greek bailout referendum

June 24, 2016
Brexit vote results announced

January 5, 2017
China's central bank warns of bitcoin's risk

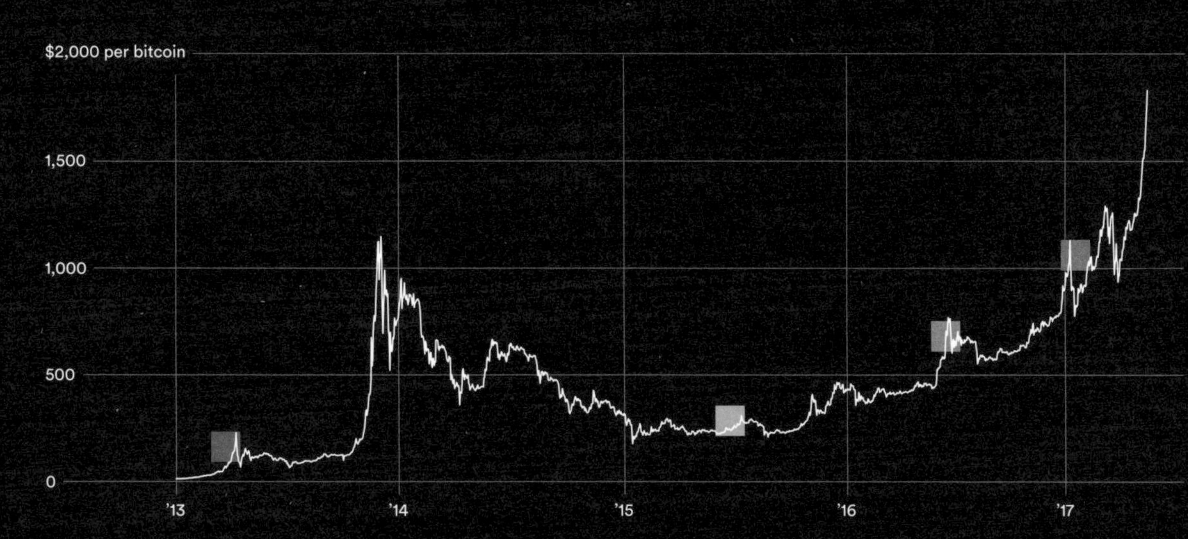

↑ Data: Coindesk. Photos: Simon Dawson/Bloomberg via Getty Images; Angelos Tzortzinis/AFP/Getty; Jeff J Mitchell/Getty; Qilai Shen/Bloomberg via Getty Images

HOW BITCOIN WORKS

Glossary for bitcoin insiders

The traders who ride bitcoin's wild swings speak a language equal parts Michael Lewis's *Liars Poker* and Reddit.

Hodl: to stay invested and not get spooked by plunging prices. It originated from a misspelled *cri de cœur* posted on the Bitcointalk forum during the great bitcoin crash of 2013: "I AM HODLING."

BearWhale: a big-time trader who thinks prices will fall. It's a dangerous creature, and has been spotted only once in the wild, trying to unload 30,000 bitcoins in a single order (worth $9 million at the time) in October 2014. Ultimately slayed by hodl-ers.

Bagholder: an investor who has been hodling for too long and is forced to face the consequences. For instance, a believer in state-issued money might be a "national fiat scrip bagholder trapped in a financial-emotional sunk-cost fallacy," to paraphrase a popular Bitcointalk forum post.

#Rekt: borrowed from online-gaming slang, to be utterly destroyed or ruined. A trader might get #rekt on margin calls.

Societies have experimented with virtual money for centuries.

Take the giant limestone disks of the Pacific island of Yap, which functioned as a currency as far back as the 16th century. As Felix Martin recounts in his book, *Money: An Unauthorized Biography*, the people of Yap came to verbal consensus over who owned which stone without actually having to move the stones, which weighed thousands of pounds, between parties. Some stones, like the one that legend says languished on the ocean floor after falling overboard during a stormy voyage, didn't even have to be seen to be used as currency.

The stone disks functioned as a virtual currency as long as the people of Yap came to an agreement about the credits and debits to be made against a particular stone. Centuries later, people are again dealing in unseen money—but this time it resides on computers scattered around the globe rather than stones dotted across a remote island.

Being virtual isn't what makes bitcoin so exceptional. Instead, bitcoin has excelled because it elegantly solves several key problems that affected earlier virtual currencies. It does this through its process of "mining," which, despite the hint of heavy industry, is really more like competitive bookkeeping.

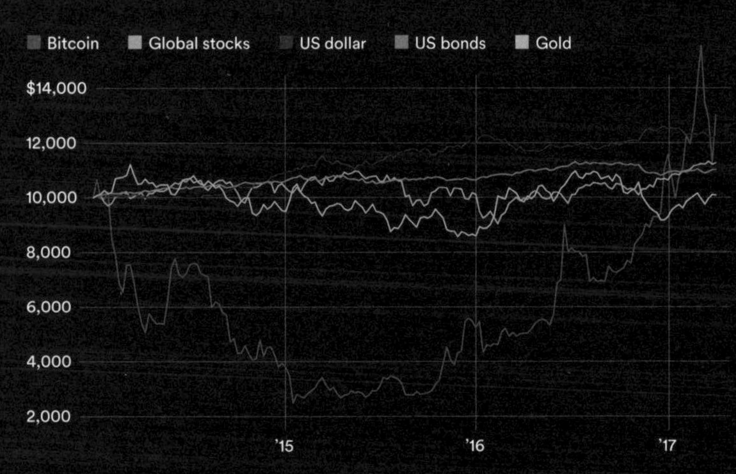

↑ If you had invested in… (Data: Bloomberg, FactSet)

Here's how it works: Every bitcoin transaction ever made is recorded in a ledger called the blockchain. This ledger is updated with a new entry roughly every 10 minutes when a new block containing a chunk of transactions is added to the chain. This universal ledger also prevents the problem of "double-spending," which allows parties to spend money they don't currently possess. (This is also the reason why banknotes come with serial numbers.) The blockchain is copied and maintained by bitcoin miners scattered across the globe, and transactions are checked against this global database to prevent fraud.

It gets competitive because there's a financial reward—currently 12.5 bitcoins—for miners who discover a new block by solving a computational puzzle. Anyone can be a bitcoin miner—it's free to run the open-source bitcoin program—but it's expensive to pay for the electricity and other costs to operate the necessary hardware. Those costs add up because as miners must beat each other at solving the puzzles, the biggest, best, and fastest machines win. Mining is now dominated by industrial miners; there are about a dozen such operators finding the majority of new blocks. In total, bitcoin mining consumes more electricity than many countries' national grids.[19] In January 2017, bitcoin miners used more electricity than Estonia, Costa Rica, or Guatemala during the same period, according to one estimate.

But you don't need a supercomputer to mine bitcoin—you can also do it yourself. Mining bitcoin by hand, as we are about to do, may not be a profitable endeavor, but there's nothing magical about the cryptographic algorithms behind bitcoin: It's just a lot of basic addition.

HERE'S HOW TO MINE BITCOIN BY HAND

Bitcoin mining is computerized guesswork. It involves repeating the same mathematical operation on a block of bitcoin transactions, with slight variations each time, until you get a certain result.

The operation is called hashing. A very simple kind of hash is to take a number like 15,465 and add up its digits: 1 + 5 + 4 + 6 + 5 = 21. Hashing a bitcoin block is basically a much more laborious version of that. As of June 2017, a bitcoin miner had to hash each block an average of about 3 x 1021 times–a 3 followed by 21 zeroes–before finding the correct solution.

Doing this without a computer would take you far longer than the age of the universe. But you can have a taste of it here. Ken Shirriff, who documents his hobby of taking apart various technologies on his popular eponymous blog, wrote a computer program that partially hashed a bitcoin block. It's almost complete, and you can fill in the blanks to finish it.

THE ACTUAL MATHEMATICS

Here's the first bit of the puzzle. A bitcoin block's metadata is shown as a series of hexadecimal numbers, labelled from A through H.

The first task is to convert those hexadecimal values to binary using the table to the right. For the sake of time, just do A, B, and C. Fill in the blanks and check your answers on the last page of this worksheet.

A	f	b	8	a	0	4	e	d
	1 1 1 1							
B	8	5	3	7	a	e	d	4
C	0	9	1	4	0	2	1	5

Next, you'll do the first step of the hash function, which is called "majority," or Maj. For each column, count the number of 1s and 0s. If there are more 1s (i.e., a majority), write a 1 in the Maj. row below. Write a 0 if there are more 0s. Fill in the blanks.

Maj.	1000	1001	0001		0000	0110	1101	0101

In the interests of space, we'll have to skip a few steps here. Three more operations will be performed on those A to H values, including shifting them around and adding them up in various ways. Each operation changes the A to H values.

After those operations are done, we end up with a new set of values for A through H:

A	05d8a5a3	B	fb8a04ed	C	8537aed4	D	09140215
+h0	6a09e667	+h1	bb67ae85	+h2	3c6ef372	+h3	a54ff53a
=	6fe28c0a	=		=	c1a6a246	=	ae63f74f
E	421030e6	F	4654a010	G	49523f55	H	a41f32e7
+h4	510e527f	+h5	9b05688c	+h6	1f83d9ab	+h7	5be0cd19
=		=	e15a089c	=		=	00000000

We must now add the new A through H values to a set of constants, h0 through h7. The tricky bit is this is all rendered in hexadecimal, and that comes with its own rules for addition.

- Hexadecimal-binary conversion chart

Hexadecimal	Binary
0	0 0 0 0
1	0 0 0 1
2	0 0 1 0
3	0 0 1 1
4	0 1 0 0
5	0 1 0 1
6	0 1 1 0
7	0 1 1 1
8	1 0 0 0
9	1 0 0 1
A	1 0 1 0
B	1 0 1 1
C	1 1 0 0
D	1 1 0 1
E	1 1 1 0
F	1 1 1 1

- Hexadecimal-decimal conversion chart

Hexadecimal	Decimal
0	0
1	1
2	2
3	3
4	4
5	5
6	6
7	7
8	8
9	9
A	1 0
B	1 1
C	1 2
D	1 3
E	1 4
F	1 5

Here's how you do it: Convert each value to a decimal using the table below. Then add together one column at a time, starting from the column furthest to the right, as you would with normal addition. If the result of the addition is 16 or greater, subtract 16 and carry 1 to the next column. Then convert back to hexadecimal. If the result is less than 16, just convert the result to hexadecimal.

So for the column furthest to the left in row A, 3 + 7 = 10. This is less than 16, so convert 10 to hexadecimal, which gives us A. The next column over is A + 6, which gives us 16 in decimal. We have to subtract 16 if the result is 16 or greater, so we get 0, and carry 1 to the next column. Simple, right? Fill in the blanks.

When you're done with that, you get eight values in hexadecimal from adding A through H to h0 through h7. Finally, in a bitcoin quirk specified by its mysterious creator, Satoshi Nakamoto, you have to reverse the result in pairs to render the block hash.

Bear in mind this was just one round of SHA-256 hashing. Hashing a block actually requires doing 128 rounds of this. And you'd have to repeat that whole cycle about 3 * 10^21 times on average to find a hash that's valid.

Shirriff was nice enough to give us a valid hash to look at. You can punch 000000000019d6689c085ae165831e934ff763ae46a2a6c172b3f1b60a8ce26f into a block explorer like Blockchain.info to look it up on the bitcoin blockchain. This particular block hash belongs to the "genesis block," which was the very first block ever mined in bitcoin, likely by Satoshi himself.

If the resulting block hash wasn't valid, you'd have to do this all over again with a new nonce—all the while racing other miners to find a valid hash. Shirriff estimates that bitcoin mining by hand results in 0.67 hashes per day. By comparison, a bitcoin-mining computer performs several terahashes (that is, a trillion hashes) per second.

SOLUTIONS:

A	f	b	8	a	0	4	e	d
	1111	1011	1000	1010	0000	0100	1110	1101
B	8	5	3	7	a	e	d	4
	1000	0101	0011	0111	1010	1110	1101	0100
C	0	9	1	4	0	2	1	5
	0000	1001	0001	0100	0000	0010	0001	0101
Maj.	1000	1001	0001	0110	0000	0110	1101	0101

A	05d8a5a3	B	fb8a04ed	C	8537aed4	D	09140215
+h0	6a09e667	+h1	bb67ae85	+h2	3c6ef372	+h3	a54ff53a
=	6fe28c0a	=	b6f1b37	=	c1a6a246	=	ae63f74f

E	421030e6	F	4654a010	G	49523f55	H	a41f32e7
+h4	510e527f	+h5	9b05688c	+h6	1f83d9ab	+h7	5be0cd19
=	931e8365	=	e15a089c	=	68d61900	=	00000000

About that cryptographic puzzle...

The exercise you just looked at is a small piece of the cryptographic algorithm that bitcoin uses, SHA-256, which is one of the most widely used algorithms in the world. Given bitcoin's ambitions to be stateless money,[20] it's ironic the algorithm was designed by the US National Security Agency in 2002.

What's in a block?

The blocks on the blockchain consist of a bundle of transactions and some metadata. This metadata includes a timestamp, a cryptographic digest of the transaction bundle, and the previous block's hash. It also includes something called a nonce—essentially a random number—that is critical to the mining process, as will be explained later.

What's a hash?

Hashing means taking a chunk of information—which could be a bitcoin block, your date of birth, or the text of the Bible—and performing lots of repeated calculations on it. The end result is a number that is always the same length (64 hexadecimal digits in SHA-256) and is unique to that chunk of information.

A hash is a one-way function: You can't work backward from the hash to figure out the original block. It's a bit like mixing paint: It's easy to mix pink and blue paint together, but it's impossible to unmix the resulting purple paint.

So why do you need a hash?

Remember that the blockchain is meant to be a tamper-proof record of all bitcoin transactions. The hash is like a seal that shows if a block has been tampered with. To be valid on the bitcoin blockchain, a hash must start with a certain number of zeroes (at least 18, as of June 2017; the number rises as more bitcoins are mined). If a block is altered, its new hash almost certainly won't be valid. A bitcoin miner's task, then, is to find a valid hash for each block.

This is where the nonce comes in. On its own, the hash of any given block won't be valid. Miners add a nonce to the block, hash it, see if the result is valid, and if not, try a different nonce. They must try a huge number of nonces—currently about 3 * 10^21—before they find one that produces the desired hash.

The work needed to do this is what they earn bitcoins for. It's also what makes the blockchain resistant to tampering—because altering a block and finding a new valid hash is just as much work as creating a new block from scratch.

[19]
Data experts estimate that a single bitcoin transaction requires as much electricity as 3.17 American households use in a day.

[20]
In April 2017, a federal judge in upstate New York ruled that bitcoin was not a currency, but rather a commodity like a collectible. Currently, the Internal Revenue Service requires that taxpayers report bitcoin trades as property, not income.

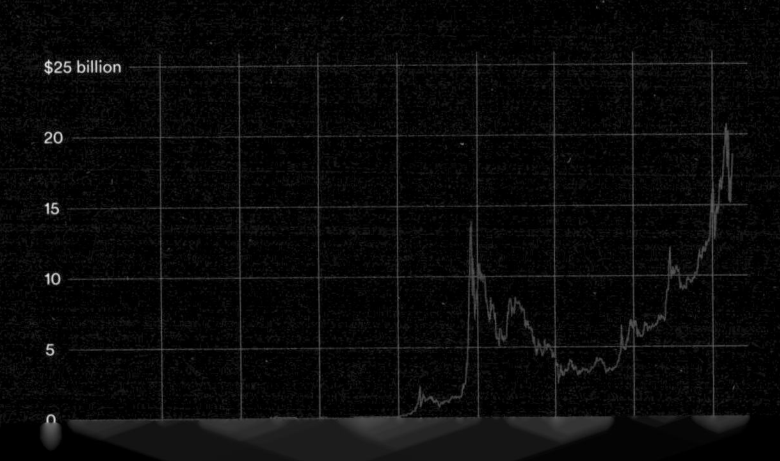

INTERVIEW WITH VITALIK BUTERIN, CREATOR OF ETHEREUM

Home-brew cryptocurrencies are a dime a dozen, with almost all touting themselves as a superior version of bitcoin, the granddaddy of cryptos.

But 23-year-old university dropout and Thiel Fellowship recipient Vitalik Buterin is the rare figure who can make that claim plausibly. He not only invented a new cryptocurrency, ethereum, but saw its market value grow to roughly $1 billion in eight months, thanks to newfangled features that make bitcoin seem old hat. The peripatetic Buterin was in Shanghai one moment and Singapore the next when we finally pinned him down for an interview. Here's what he had to say about ethereum's future.

Ethereum, like bitcoin, depends on miners to keep transactions flowing. There are inherent risks to this model, so what are you doing to make ethereum as robust as possible?

We're looking heavily at proof of stake [a radically different type of consensus algorithm] and I think in the long term it's going to be crucial for security. Because as time goes on, I'm becoming more and more concerned about just how secure mining actually is.

What's the concern?

In the case of bitcoin, 70% of the hash power is in China. If the People's Bank of China at some point decided that it wanted to shut bitcoin down, it could basically force all these mining farms to participate in a huge attack over and over again, to the point where bitcoin has to hardfork [an irrevocable split in bitcoin's transaction history, creating two versions of bitcoin] to another kind of proof of work. You could easily kill the protocol.

There's an idea of cryptocurrencies being "fat protocols," where more value is captured at the protocol rather than the application layer. What do you think of this?

Protocols like SSL and email and so forth all create a huge amount of value. But it's not about value creation—it's actually a story of value capture. The interesting thing with a lot of these blockchain protocols is that, for the first time, you have a way to create protocols that actually manage to fund themselves in some way. If this kind of approach takes off, it could end up drastically increasing the quality of bottom-level protocols that we use to interact with each other in various ways.

Do you ever wish you were anonymous like bitcoin creator Satoshi Nakamoto?

I think honestly that would just be too hard and I'm the sort of person where if I had to hide all my life from people, I would just get way too lonely too quickly.

Tracking diamonds with blockchains

In 2015, Leanne Kemp started Everledger, a company that's putting diamonds and other rarities on a blockchain. The idea is to bind a material object with a digital identity that leaves a permanent, tamper-proof, digital record.

Everledger works with certified diamonds, which are stones that have been analyzed and inscribed with a unique serial number. It collects over 40 data points on the unique characteristics and shape of each stone, linking these to the stone's serial number.

A unique identifier is generated and included in a bitcoin transaction of a single satoshi, which is a hundredth of a millionth of a bitcoin. Once the transaction is completed by miners, a record of the diamond is permanently stamped on the bitcoin blockchain.

While Everledger records every diamond's identifier on the bitcoin blockchain, which is publicly accessible, it maintains a parallel, private blockchain to store ownership and other information. It's a clever workaround that combines the promise of bitcoin's public database and the safeguards that can be added to a private, blockchain-without-bitcoin version.

THE DOMINANCE OF BITCOIN

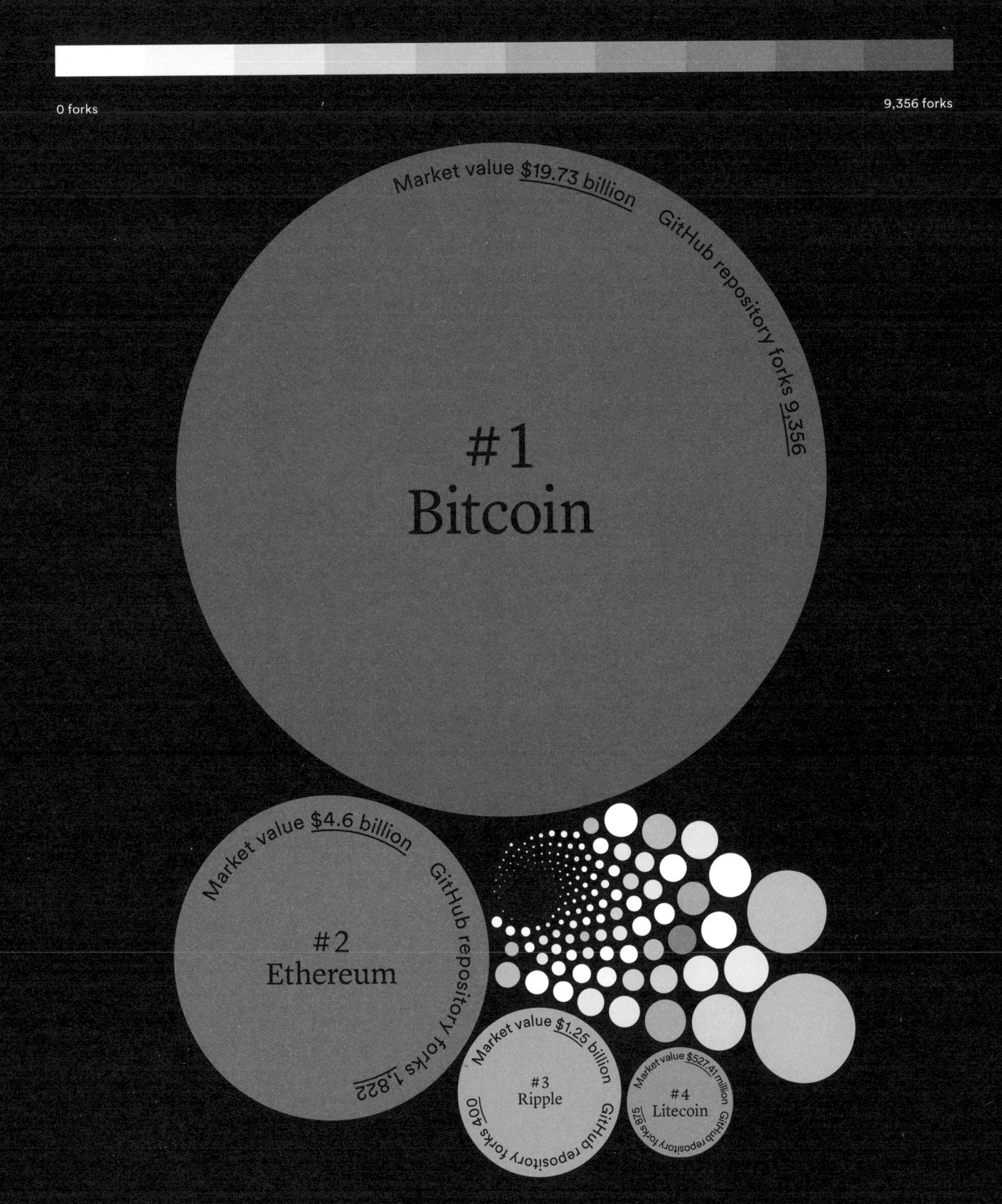

This visualization ranks 31 cryptocurrencies by their attractiveness to speculators and software developers. A circle's size shows its value in the market on April 18, 2017. Its color indicates how much technical work has been invested in it, as represented by the number of times it's been copied by programmers—what's known as "forking"—on GitHub, the world's most popular site for sharing open-source software. (Data: CryptoCompare, Coinmarketcap.com)

COUNTERFEITING CURRENCIES SINCE 7TH CENTURY BC

- 7th century BC
  Lydia (now Turkey)

Lydia's early coins were made of electrum and valued by weight. Counterfeiters would inject the core of smaller coins with less-precious metals—they were already so light that it was hard to notice the difference.

- 13th century
  China

Early paper money used in China was printed on large sheets of paper derived from the wood of mulberry trees. To deter counterfeiters, the empire had to station soldiers around mulberry forests.

- 15th-16th centuries
  Aztec Empire,

As cocoa beans were rare and desirable, they thus served as a means of payment. Counterfeiters stuffed their husks with mud or other worthless substances that had a similar weight and kept the precious—and tasty—seeds for eating or drinking.

- 1860s
  United States

During the American Civil War, entrepreneurs in the Union did a roaring trade in fake Confederate banknotes, which were not accepted in the North. The counterfeits were initially pitched as souvenirs but quickly made their way south and destabilized the economy.

- 1942
  Germany

During World War II, prisoners at concentration camps in Nazi Germany were put to work producing near-perfect forgeries of the British pound. Although a plan to flood Britain with the notes never came to fruition, the few that were identified in circulation stoked fear among British officials.

- 1980s-2000s
  Canada

In 1986, Canada introduced banknote designs to thwart color photocopiers, which were growing in popularity (and falling in price). Technology soon caught up, and Canada went from having fewer than five fakes per million in 1990 to nearly 500 fakes per million in the early 2000s.

Left:
An Aztec stone figure of a man carrying a cacao pod, originally from Amatlan, Veracruz, Mexico.
(Circa 1440-1521, courtesy of the Granger Collection)

Right:
A World War II-era counterfeit British banknote.
(Public Domain/Wikimedia)

TURBOPUMP

How space became profitable

Hidden from view, the turbopump is the heart that powers nearly everything humans do in space.

Turbopumps allow rocket engines to throttle up and down, or turn off and on again, by using liquefied propellants like oxygen and hydrogen, forced together in a very hot and very high-pressure combustion chamber. Their ability to marshal the tremendous forces involved in space travel without being destroyed themselves epitomizes the challenges facing rocket companies.

Turbopumps are among the components that firms including SpaceX, Blue Origin, and Rocket Lab are reinventing in order to make reusable rockets. New, stronger materials make components durable for multiple launches, and techniques like 3D printing are paring down production costs. Today's rocket launches discard spent boosters worth $100 million or more. Reusable boosters could cut the cost of getting cargo to space from tens of thousands to as little as thousands—or even hundreds—of dollars per kilogram.

Reducing cost is the primary fixation of the new space race—a global stampede to be not the first in flight but the biggest in the market. Cheaper spaceflight would make business beyond the atmosphere feasible for all kinds of companies, from broadband-internet providers and imaging satellites to orbital hotels and manufacturing facilities.

But low-cost and robust don't always go together, and companies will need to be wary in balancing the trade-offs. After all, NASA's Space Shuttle promised a similar vision: a reusable craft to bring society into space. But its designers turned out to be too optimistic about the costs and dangers of reuse. Both the technology and demand for access to space have made big leaps, but failure is still a very public and costly affair. Can the private sector now do what the government couldn't?

↑ 3D-printed turbopump with astronaut. (Mathery)

THE TWISTED TRAJECTORY OF A REUSABLE ROCKET

Second-stage cargo

A common second-stage cargo for SpaceX is the reusable Dragon spacecraft, which supplies the International Space Station (ISS). When the rocket reaches space, the two stages separate. The first heads back to Earth and the second takes the payload to its destination on just one engine.

Grid fins

Four grid fins that steer the rocket down are key to bringing the first stage back to Earth. These unusually shaped devices are optimized to steer objects flying faster than the speed of sound.

Turbopump

There are nine engines with turbopumps similar to this one in the first stage of the Falcon 9. Together, they produce over 1 million lbs (4.45 million newtons) of thrust at sea level to break free of gravity. The cost of the high-precision manufacturing needed to do that is a major incentive for reuse.

Landing legs

Unfolding landing legs deploy just before a reusable rocket touches down. Weighing around 500 kg (1,100 lbs) each, they are strong enough together to support the 14-story-tall first stage on a landing pad or a floating barge.

The key to cutting the cost of space travel is reusing orbital rockets. In March 2017, US company SpaceX launched and landed the first previously flown commercial orbital rocket, a milestone in space history. The Falcon 9 rocket has two parts, called stages, that together fly their payload into space. SpaceX is able to reuse the first stage, which is the largest and most expensive, but it hopes to begin reusing the smaller second stage, too. How much money could be saved? While SpaceX's competitors sell rides on their rockets for more than $100 million, a lift on SpaceX's reusable rocket is expected to start at less than $45 million.

THE HOMEGROWN TECHNOLOGY BEHIND INDIA'S FAST-GROWING SPACE INDUSTRY

Space janitors

"Space trash," the detritus left by retired satellites and discarded rocket parts, zooms around Earth at speeds of up to 28,000 km (17,400 miles) per hour. Twenty-thousand of those free-floating fragments are larger than a fist, according to NASA, and while the Union of Concerned Scientists lists only seven serious collisions between spacecraft and space trash from 1990 to 2010, one big hit could cause serious damage to a shuttle or satellite.

Astroscale, founded in 2013 by entrepreneur Mitsunobu Okada and based in Singapore, is the world's first startup dedicated to cleaning up debris. The first of two satellites it is building, IDEA OSG 1, is set to launch in 2018. Wrapped with a thin sensor film, the satellite will record the size and location of each fragment it bumps into to produce a map that other companies might use to position their satellites out of harm's way. A second satellite is being designed with adhesive to actually catch debris.

Janitorial work isn't the most glamorous venture in commercial space, but Astroscale's workers believe in their mission. "Space is getting crowded," says project manager Masahiko Uetsuhara. "We have to clean it if we want to have constellations of satellites, like those planned by SpaceX and LeoSat."

The Polar Satellite Launch Vehicle wasn't always one of the world's most reliable rockets. During its 1993 maiden launch, there was a glitch between the second and third stages of the rocket after it took off, and the mission failed.

Over the next 25 years, however, the PSLV charted an incredible trajectory with dozens of successful launches. Its most recent achievement came in 2017 when it carried 104 satellites on a single launch vehicle—a world record.

The persevering PSLV reflects the steady rise of India's space program and the success of its frugal, homegrown technology. When India launched its Mars mission in 2014 at a cost of just Rs450 crore ($70 million), it used a PSLV rocket to launch the orbiter into space.

The PSLV also provides India's space agency, the Indian Space Research Organisation, with opportunities to make some money at a time when the world is straining to send stuff into space as cheaply as possible. The 44 satellites it launched between 2014 and 2016 for foreign customers in eight countries generated close to €100 million ($112 million) in revenue.

One of its newest customers is a private domestic startup, TeamIndus, which was founded in Bengaluru in 2011 to compete for the $30 million Google Lunar X Prize. The prize will go to the first privately funded team that successfully lands a spacecraft on the moon, travels at least 500 meters (1,640 ft) across the moon's surface, and beams back data and images to Earth.

TeamIndus's 100 employees variously describe themselves as young colts and older, ISRO-trained "Jedi masters." They plan to build small satellites (the company estimates it can slash satellite costs by between 30% and 35%) and might someday attempt to put people in space.

With the financial backing of a who's-who of Indian business leaders, including Infosys co-founder Nandan Nilekani, Ratan Tata of the Tata Group, and Sachin Bansal and Binny Bansal of Flipkart, Team Indus isn't short of funds to take its big leap. But first it needs a launch. And for that, it already has a contract for a lift on the PSLV.

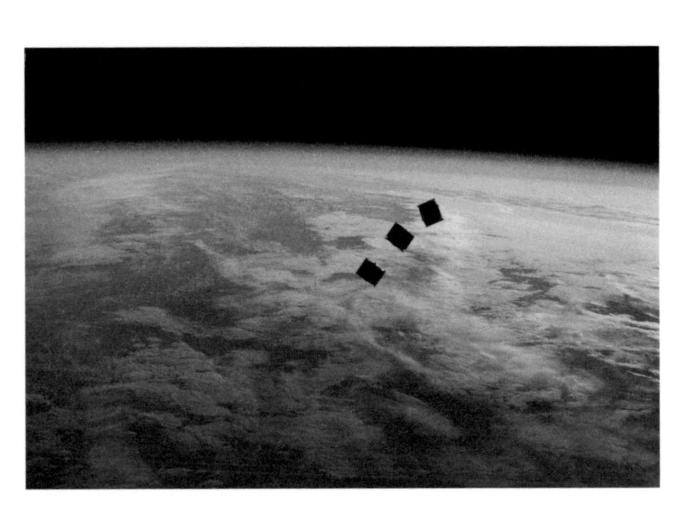

↑ Several tiny satellites, released outside the Japanese Kibo Laboratory, are photographed by an Expedition 33 crew member on the International Space Station. (Oct. 4, 2012, NASA)

THE RACE TO REVIVE A 30-YEAR-OLD SCHEME FOR SATELLITE INTERNET

Satellite broadcasting is the biggest business in space. But as every kind of media goes digital, the smartest companies in the world are betting billions of dollars on a nearly 30-year-old scheme to deliver internet by satellite, too.

While airliners, cruise ships, and people in off-the-grid locations already rely on satellite internet, most of us don't, simply because connection through underground fiber-optic cables is faster. It takes whole seconds for data to traverse the 22,000 miles (35,400 km) or more to the satellites flying far above Earth.

Space internet startups like OneWeb, SpaceX, and Boeing think they have a fix for that. They envision networks of hundreds of relatively cheap satellites in low-Earth orbit, just a few hundred miles above the ground. Flying at high speeds, they could handle internet traffic for millions of users around the world who currently have no or limited internet access.

During the US's 1990s tech boom, a company called Teledesic, backed by Microsoft executives, tried a similar plan and wound up bankrupt. But demand for internet access is higher now, and space engineers say that several trends give the plan more credibility this time around: It costs less to get to space; microprocessors that handle the data and batteries that fuel them are both smaller and more powerful; and advances in satellite-antenna technology and computer networking make it easier to share internet traffic across the system.

The leader in this race is serial entrepreneur Greg Wyler and his company OneWeb. The firm is first in line to be assigned exclusive use by the International Telecommunication Union to transmit data from space. In April 2016, it broke ground on a factory in Florida to mass produce satellites for $1 million a pop. (Modern communication satellites typically cost tens of millions.) Now, after receiving a $1 billion investment from the Japanese conglomerate Softbank in December 2016, OneWeb is combining with an established satellite company, Intelsat, that would leave Wyler as the executive chairman of the new firm.

↓ A crack on the ISS caused by space debris. (April 2016, Tim Peake/ESA/NASA)

The race to reinvent satellite internet is risky: Despite rising demand for internet access, analysts are skeptical that there will be room in this market for multiple networks. The prize for first place is billions of dollars in revenue, but finishing second or third won't mean a smaller slice of the market—it will mean failure.

A satellite's-eye view

Roughly 20,000 storage tanks around the world contain the global reserve of crude oil. As the tanks are drained, their lids gradually sink. A few years ago, US satellite-imaging startup Orbital Insight realized that the change in shadows cast by the floating roof on each could serve as an indicator of the supply inside.

Orbital Insight now feeds satellite imagery of the lids' shadows into sophisticated software to generate real-time assessments of global oil reserves—something clients in the financial and energy industries are happy to pay for. "It's an answer the next time someone asks you what trigonometry is good for," says founder James Crawford.

Similar technology is at work for the handful of other imagery companies combining the insights of big data with pictures taken from space. With the help of their services, farmers, for example, can better plan for the future by getting precise measurementsw of the amount of corn being grown in their region at any one time, and the World Bank can measure poverty by analyzing building density, crop health, the number of cars, and other factors. (Courtesy of Orbital Insight/Digital Globe)

On July 16, 2015, NASA sent a camera 1.5 million kilometers (932,000 miles) into space to take this image of the dark side of our moon with Earth luminous in the background. The camera is part of satellite DSCOVR (the Deep Space Climate Observatory), which sits in a special orbit between Earth and the sun. It collects data on terrestrial climate change and weather patterns and also monitors solar storms that can wipe out vital electrical systems on Earth. DSCOVR was launched by a SpaceX Falcon 9 as the company's first payload beyond Earth's orbit. (NASA)

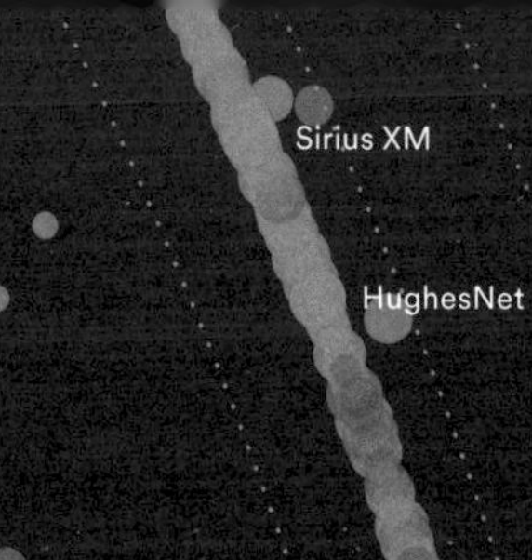

Sirius XM

Sirius XM

Consumer internet in space is a tricky business: Only a few companies (HughesNet, ViaSat, and Wildblue) provide the service directly using high-altitude satellites. Upstarts have a bad orbital omen in the Sky Terra satellite, launched by now-bankrupt Lightsquared.

rks satellites
d internet
emerging

Sky Terra

20,000
30,000
40,000
50,000
60,000
70,000
80,000
90,000
100,000
200,000
300,000 km

Sky Terra

ViaSat

HughesNet

Wildblue

Civil
Commercial
Government
Military

Launch weight
<3
5,000
20,000 kg

Not known

ellation
to more than
strial listeners.

(Data: Union of Concerned Scientists, NASA, Zarya, N2YO.com, Claude Lafleur. Sept. 1, 2015)

Sirius XM

Sirius XM

ALL OF THE SATELLITES ORBITING EARTH

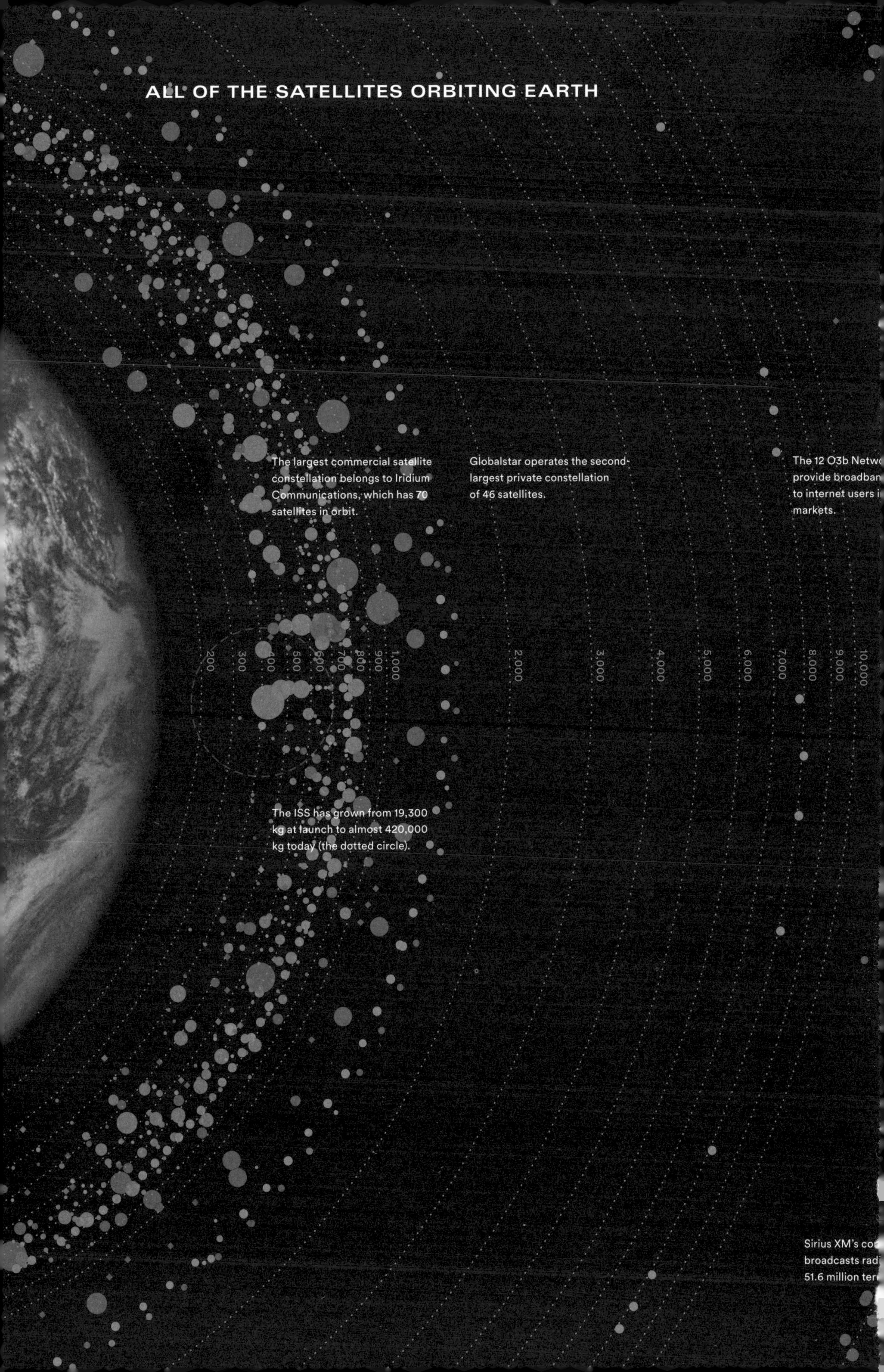

The largest commercial satellite constellation belongs to Iridium Communications, which has 70 satellites in orbit.

Globalstar operates the second-largest private constellation of 46 satellites.

The 12 O3b Netw
provide broadban
to internet users i
markets.

200 300 400 500 600 700 800 900 1,000 2,000 3,000 4,000 5,000 6,000 7,000 8,000 9,000 10,000

The ISS has grown from 19,300 kg at launch to almost 420,000 kg today (the dotted circle).

Sirius XM's co
broadcasts rad
51.6 million ter

US SPACE TRAVEL IN FOUR HISTORIC SUITS

THE ORIGINAL PRESSURE SUIT (1934)

The first pressurized suit was used in 1934 by US airplane pilot Wiley Post so that he could pursue speed records at altitudes too high for humans to survive without protection. (1935, courtesy of the Smithsonian National Air and Space Museum)

BILL DANA'S PINK BOOTS (1975)

No fashion is free from the tyranny of gender. When US test pilot Bill Dana quipped in 1975 that white boots weren't masculine enough for an astronaut, the David Clark company sent him pink ones to wear instead. (Courtesy of NASA)

MANNED MANEUVERING UNIT (1984)

The MMU is a backpack-sized jetpack that allowed US astronauts to do space construction work without being tethered to their spacecraft. It was tested three times, but NASA eventually decided it would be safer and simpler to use robots or a simple tether to perform work outside. Astronauts still carry a smaller version on spacewalks for emergency use. (1983, courtesy of NASA)

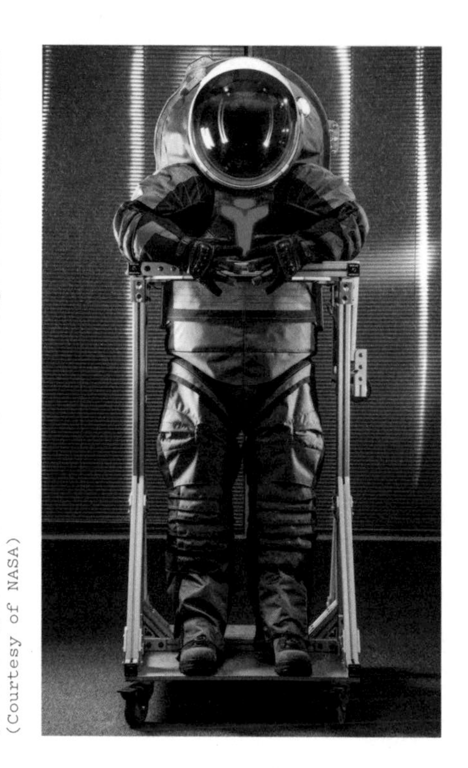

Z-2 (2017)

NASA is developing a planetary-exploration suit called the Z-2, for which astronauts will be able to 3D print replacement parts in space. You climb into it through a hatch in the back. (Courtesy of NASA)

In the vacuum of space, a human being is liable to freeze, boil, and asphyxiate, all at the same time. A pressurized suit can save you, but the challenge is making one that allows the astronaut to interact with the world. Imagine trying to move around while encased in a rigid, rubber bubble; even trained NASA astronauts wind up soaked in sweat doing simple repairs on the ISS. If humans are going to start spending more time in space, we're going to need better suits.

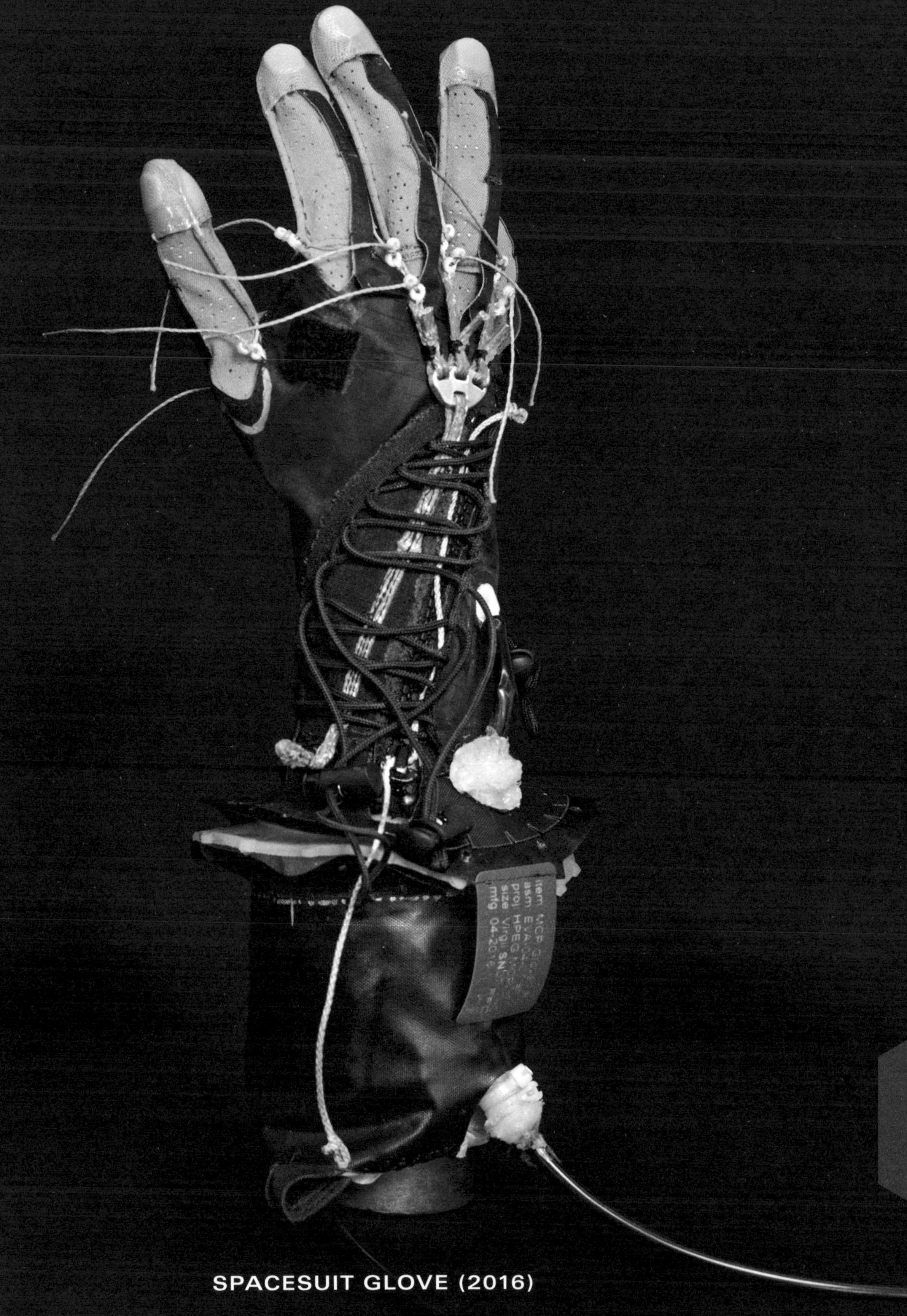

SPACESUIT GLOVE (2016)

Protecting the human hand while allowing it a full range of motion is the hardest part of designing a space suit. Brooklyn-based maker Final Frontier Designs, founded by an American and a Russian, is working with NASA on pressurized elastic gloves that don't have to be inflated. This photograph is of a mechanical counter-pressure glove in their Brooklyn studio. (May 2017, Johnny Simon for Quartz)

"WELCOME HOME" BREAD (КАРАВАЙ)

↓ Dennis Tito, the world's first space tourist, tastes bread with salt during a traditional ceremony in Star City outside Moscow on May 16, 2001. (AFP/Getty)

Astronauts of all nationalities who visit the ISS also get a taste of *karavai*. For decades, a pre-made version of this bread has been offered to astronauts boarding the station or when returning to Earth. The first reported offering of karavai in space took place on Sept. 20, 1980 when a Cuban and Soviet astronaut were greeted with bread and salt as they boarded the orbiting Soviet Salyut 6 space station. Traditionally served to guests in Russia, the bread represents hospitality and the salt symbolizes friendship in several cultures.

Ingredients:

1¾ cup warm milk
½ oz yeast
2¼ lbs wheat flour
2 large eggs
⅔ cup sugar
⅓ lb butter, melted
salt

Instructions:

- Dissolve the yeast in one cup of warm milk, add half of the flour, and blend carefully.
- Sprinkle with flour and leave in a warm place for 2-3 hours.
- When the leavening doubles, add the eggs, salt, sugar, and the remaining ¾ cup of milk.
- Add the rest of the flour and the melted butter.
- Knead carefully.
- Let the dough rise until it has doubled, then punch and let rise again.
- Divide the dough into small oblong balls and decorate with leaves and flowers.
- Bake in a preheated oven at 190°F (90°C).

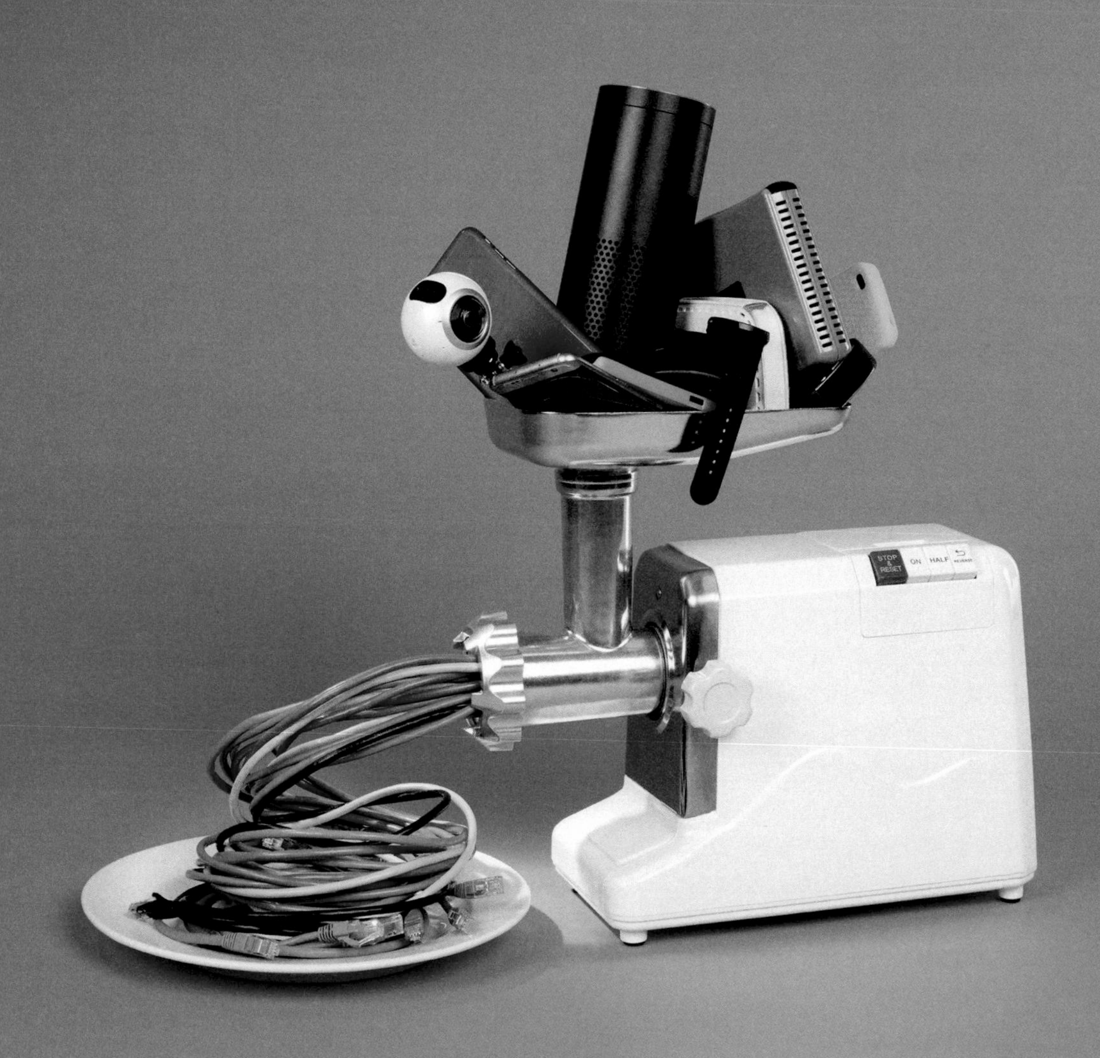
STOP
&
RESET
ON
HALF

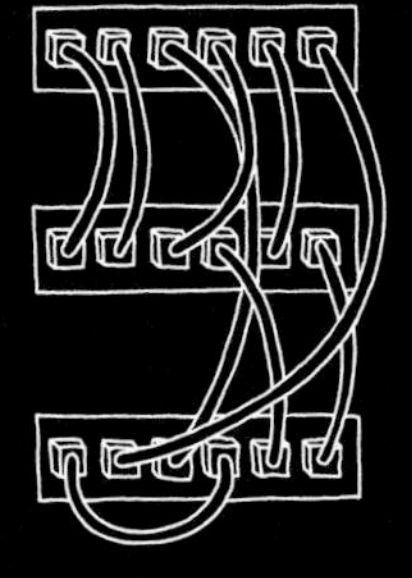

SERVER FARM

The heart of the internet

When we think of our data as living in "the cloud," we may imagine a weightless ether with infinite storage capacity. But the reality is far more prosaic: large, windowless buildings containing thousands of computers. The internet's physical interface looks a lot more like industrial farming than cloud watching.

These buildings are data centers—or, to use the industry parlance, server farms. They are the hubs from which fiber-optic cables spread out, connecting to other server farms in a radial pattern replicated thousands of times across the globe.

Where server farms were once largely interchangeable (everyone on the internet was a renter in one), a property-owning class has increasingly emerged. Server farms belonging to Google, Amazon, Facebook, and their ilk are built to serve the interests of these hugely powerful companies. Through these structures, the world's tech companies can ensure their videos flow more smoothly to their users, rent computational power out to smaller players, and sometimes decide what gets seen by the population of one country or another.

While server farms deliver global influence to some companies, they are also uniquely vulnerable. Cables can break if there is an earthquake, for example, and silicon can melt in a fire. Fluctuations in the price of electricity might also make the cost of running a farm untenable in some situations. Thus, there is the need for various levels of redundancy: These range from common-sense solutions, like duplicates of servers, to extreme ones, like copying data to be held in separate buildings.

These material dangers are why companies scout for the lowest-risk locations for their farms, pay for green energy to power them, and take advantage of special financial structures to wring money from them. In these ways, server farms have become more than merely the hubs of the internet: They're catalysts for innovation and development right across the global economy.

MASSIVE SERVER FARMS ARE DRIVING SILICON VALLEY'S RACE TO RENEWABLES

The tech industry is one of the most vocal about lowering carbon footprints, but a recent global data explosion has made the issue more pressing. While processing and data storage currently account for about 2% of global electricity usage, research from Sweden indicates demand is growing so fast that the level could rise to 13% by 2030.

Facebook was one of the first big tech firms to set a goal of sourcing energy from renewables in 2011. Its plans were quickly surpassed by Google and Apple, which in 2012 set the goal of reaching 100% renewable power for their entire operations. Now Google, the world's biggest corporate buyer of renewable electricity with annual contracts to purchase 2.6 gigawatts, is on course to powering all of its offices and server farms using renewables by 2017.

Gary Demasi, who directs location strategy for Google's data centers and manages the company's energy investments, was part of early conversations about how to become sustainable. "We fundamentally believe that climate change is real. It's an issue that we as a sort of global citizen have a responsibility to help address," Demasi says.

The way renewable power is bought—by using very long-term, fixed-price contracts called power-purchase agreements—also appeals to companies that know they'll be using a lot of electricity in the future. That's one reason why it's easier for a tech giant to use renewables than a smaller business. Not all companies can plan 30 years out, and not all utility providers have the infrastructure or are willing to spend the money to offer renewable energy, even if customers ask for it.

But smaller companies can also drive innovation. By 2016, only one US server-farm operator, the Arizona-based Switch, had achieved the target of sourcing all its power from renewables. Like Google, Switch wants to base all its operations on renewable energy that's generated as close as possible to where it's used. It fought a long battle with local utility NV Energy to make that possible.

Tech companies would probably not have made as much progress were it not for a recent, dramatic drop in renewable-energy prices. Since Google signed its first contract in 2010, global wind prices have dropped 60% and global solar prices 80%.

↑ A server rack in New York City. (xPACIFICA/Getty)

Custom clouds

Before the rise of cloud computing, big tech companies bought their servers from well-known brands like HP, Dell, and IBM. But these American brands weren't actually manufacturing the servers—that work was outsourced to original design manufacturers (ODMs), which are factories skilled in making hardware products and are often based in Taiwan.

Internet giants have now cut out the middlemen and are working directly with these factories to build custom-made servers. Companies like Facebook and Amazon work with Taiwanese contractors like Wistron, Foxconn, and Quanta to make servers tailored to their specific needs. For example, a buyer might decide its next 250,000 servers don't need a video-monitor connector. This could save them 30 cents and a few watts of power per server—small chippings that add up.

According to research firm IDC, about 17% of server shipments in 2015 went straight from the factory to the business that used them, up from about 5% in 2009.

However, all the software and maintenance for the servers is still controlled by the internet giants. Once a server is out the door, the relationship with the manufacturer ends. For all the savings Taiwan's server makers provide cloud companies, they're reaping few of the long-term benefits.

IT'S NEARLY IMPOSSIBLE TO FIND A GOOD PLACE FOR A SERVER FARM

Finding the perfect location for a data center is practically impossible. Build in Luleå, Sweden, where Facebook opened a data center in 2013, or Odense, Denmark, where the company is building a second Scandinavian facility, and you save money on electricity by using the cold Arctic air to cool your machines. The location also means it's able to serve its audience in Europe more efficiently. But the trade-off is access: There aren't many direct flights connecting San Francisco to a small town at the edge of the Arctic Circle.

↑ Radio antennas at the ALMA project in Chile's Atacama desert. (March 2013, Martin Bernetti/AFP/Getty)

Build in California, and you're in good company: The state houses the largest number of data centers in the US—more than 800. But if you place your data center on the San Andreas fault, it becomes vulnerable to earthquakes.

According to a 2015 report commissioned by London-based data-center provider Zenium, executives in the UK, Germany, and Turkey think physical security is second only to cost when evaluating a location for data centers. Nevertheless, only 45% of their facilities are flood-proof and only 43% are earthquake-proof. That explains why almost half of the executives surveyed had problems with natural disasters in the previous decade, with the most expensive incident costing £500,000 ($640,000).

So how do companies decide where to build their powerhouses? It depends on their priorities. For high-frequency traders, relative location matters most. Placing a data center a couple of meters closer or farther from a stock exchange can mean millions earned or lost. According to Michael Lewis's *Flash Boys*, traders connected a data center in Chicago with a stock exchange in New Jersey through the shortest and straightest fiber-optic cable possible, even if that meant laying it through mountains. But for people in other industries, the priority can be constant availability, protection against natural disasters, proper security, environmental friendliness, or energy efficiency.

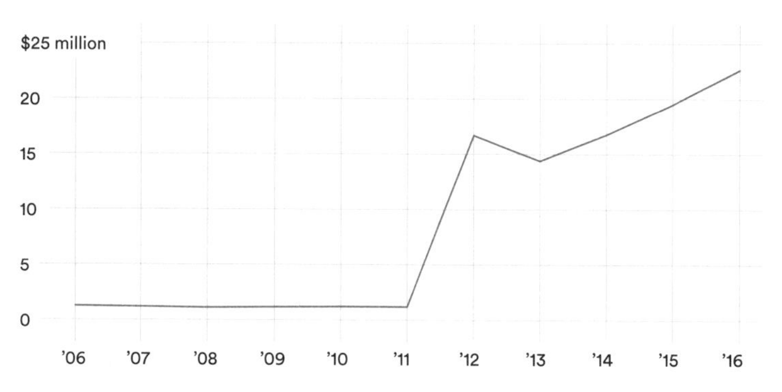

↑ Wage income from information jobs in Crook County, Oregon. Data: Quarterly Census of Employment and Wages

Prineville nights

In Prineville, Oregon, the evenings are never hot. Even in July, when daytime temperatures reach 86°F (30°C), the average nightly low in Prineville is under 50°F. Cold air fills the city of nearly 10,000 people every evening. Now it also fills Facebook data centers.

Attracted by a climate that's ideal for energy efficiency, Facebook began constructing data centers in Oregon's high desert in 2011. As of 2017, Facebook had built four in Prineville, totalling an area of over 1 million sq ft (93,000 million sq meters). Apple also started building data centers in Prineville in 2013.

The data centers are designed to take advantage of their surroundings. Todd Flack, Facebook's Prineville site manager, explains that the sides of the buildings have openings so that air can flow in during the evenings. After the air enters the building, it's filtered and adjusted to the proper humidity before being dropped right on the servers to cool them.

Facebook's Prineville data centers employ about 200 people full-time, and Apple has at least another 100 workers. The city's economy had been devastated by a declining timber industry, but it is now rebounding through this accident of climate. Largely due to the server farms, wages in Crook County, of which Prineville is the county seat, are among the fastest growing of any in Oregon.

A BUNKER, A CHURCH, AND A BARGE: STRANGE HOMES FOR DATA

Located in Switzerland, where data privacy is a constitutional right, the Deltalis data center is protected both physically and politically—it's in a Cold War-era bunker inside a granite mountain in the Swiss Alps.

The ALMA astronomical observatory's data center in the Atacama Desert is one of the highest data centers in the world, at 2,900 meters (9,500 ft). Operated by Cisco, the building receives oxygen injections because of its altitude, and machines are made to withstand earthquake vibrations.

Constructed in 1975, the Verizon Building in New York City had to be retrofitted with new infrastructure and upgraded power to host the Sabey-operated Intergate Manhattan data center.

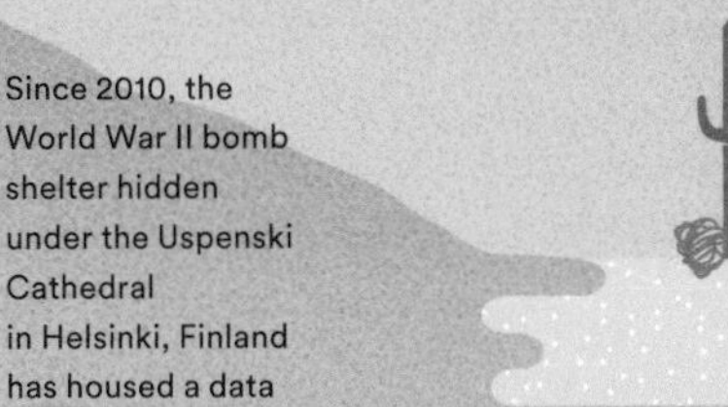

Since 2010, the World War II bomb shelter hidden under the Uspenski Cathedral in Helsinki, Finland has housed a data center built by Academica before being acquired by Telecity and then Equinix. The facility sends excess heat produced by the machines to heat homes in Helsinki.

The Altamonte Springs municipal data center in Florida was moved to a water tank with eight-inch-thick concrete walls in 2005 to protect it from hurricanes.

The Nautilus Technologies floating data center is currently being built at a former Navy shipyard in Vallejo, California. The facility, expected to be completed in 2017, will use seawater for cooling.

The data center for the IceCube particle detector, which looks for particles generated by cosmic events such as star explosions, is located at a US research station in Antarctica. Ice protects it from natural radiation and helps detect light emitted by particles.

BETTING THE FARM ON A SERVER FARM

[21]
Up to 70% of global internet traffic travels through Loudoun County, Virginia, population 350,000. Much of that traffic is routed through machines owned by Amazon Web Services, the largest hosting company operating today, meaning an outage there usually affects huge portions of the web.

"The cloud" that stores so much of our digital life is not an ephemeral mass of data suspended over cities and towns. In reality, it's a series of windowless buildings containing masses of servers in towns like Slough outside of London and North Bergen in New Jersey.[21]

For over a decade, there's been an effort to make these data centers even more abstract by turning them into publicly listed, tradable instruments known as real-estate investment trusts, or REITs. This particular vehicle allows investors to buy slivers of a property portfolio and gain regular dividend payouts. In 2016, share prices of data-center REITs hit all-time highs, lifted by surging internet activity that increasingly relies on the cloud and corporations needing their own facilities.

There are currently six publicly traded data-center REITs in the US, with Equinix being the largest of them by market cap. It has performed heroically since adopting its trust structure in 2015 (it was previously listed as a data-center operator), rising 71% by the end of 2016.

Data centers cluster where fiber connectivity meets risk-free physical space. Take Slough, for instance, a suburb located 34 km (21 miles) west of London. It's home to dozens of data centers, some operated by REITs and others run by banks and firms with intensive computational or security needs.

"Within one square kilometer in Slough, there are probably 26 to 27 data centers," says Mark Trevor, a real-estate broker at Cushman and Wakefield in London.

The factors that go into picking a location for a data center are rooted in esoteric risk forecasts. Weighing those risks is the job of Gary Boyd at Rackspace, a large data-center operator. "You will rarely find a data center next to a large petrochemical facility or storage," he says. "There's too much risk of an accident."

Data-center REITs gained 26% in 2016 compared to the broader FTSE NAREIT All Equity REITs index, which gained roughly 9%. As these REITs continue to catch on with investors, the property game of the future will be less about what makes a good mall or portfolio of homes. Instead, it's going to be about the locations that are the most attractive for the machines that connect our world.[22]

[22]
In 2017, IBM scientists devised a method to store data on an atom. Their research demonstrated the ability to turn a single atom into a magnet that can then be encoded with a single bit of data. IBM's still-experimental technology would allow all of iTunes' 35 million songs to fit on a hard drive the size of a credit card.

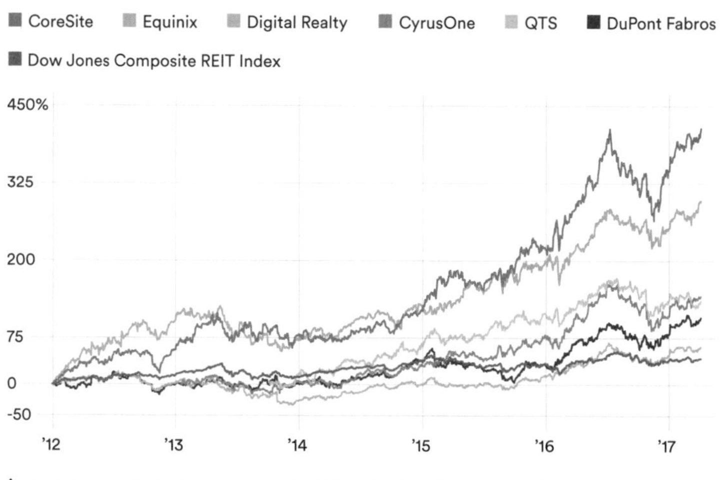

↑ Performance of US-listed data-center REITs, 2012-2016. Data: FactSet

HOW STATES CENSOR, SPY ON, AND SHUT DOWN THE INTERNET

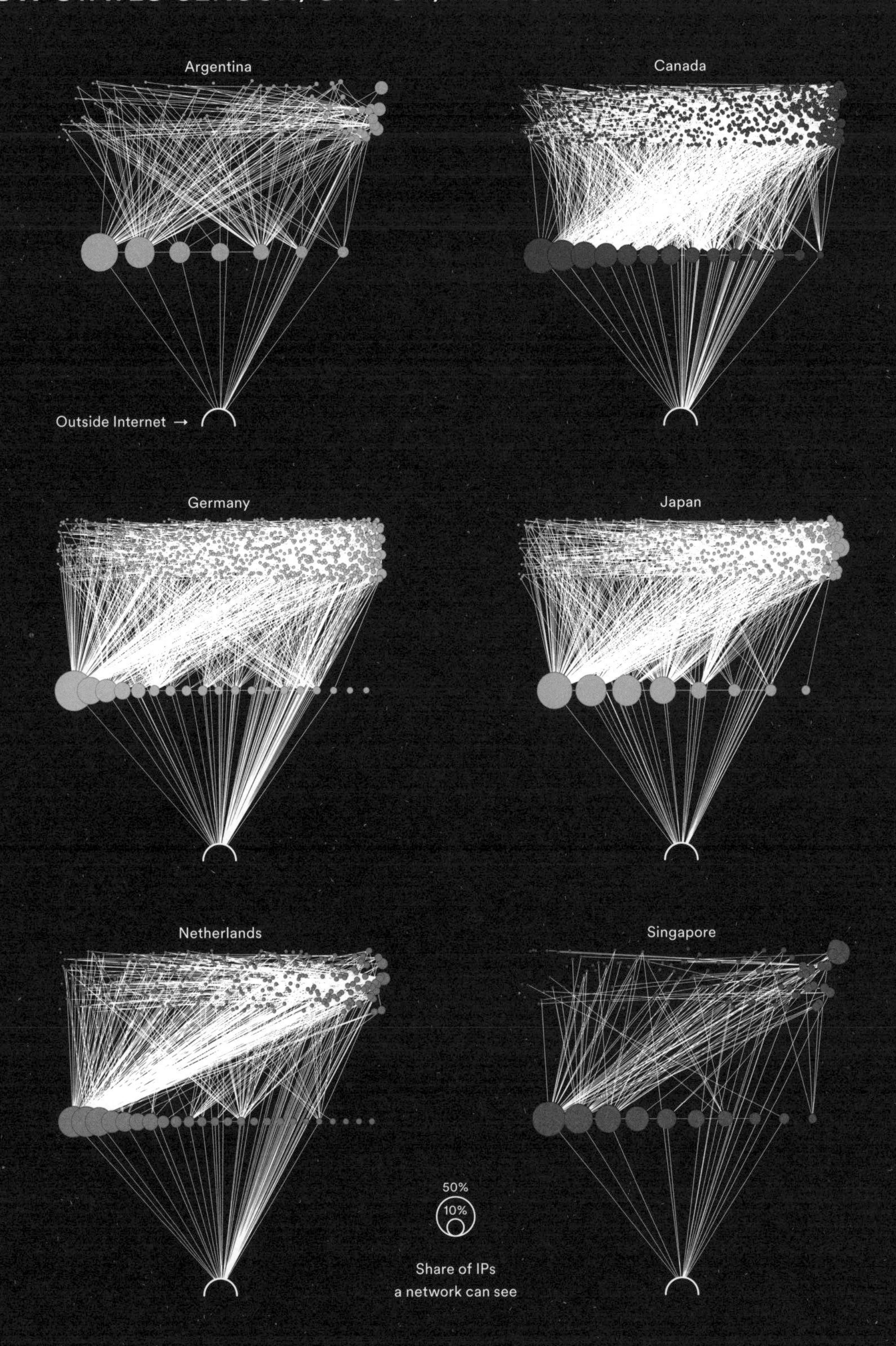

The physical systems that make up the internet's infrastructure are a lot more centralized than you might think. Users can access the internet through any number of networks, usually controlled by internet service providers (ISPs), universities, or businesses. But on their way from point A to point B, they almost always have to stop at a centrally located autonomous system, or AS, that handles huge amounts of traffic. These internet choke points are responsible for sending traffic along the network, meaning data becomes centralized, even if it is just passing through. Researchers at Harvard University attempted to determine how easily a given country's government could control its internet by looking at the proportion of IP addresses—unique identifiers given to each device connected to the internet—that flow through major choke points. Their research, published in 2011, analyzed trace routes, which are actual paths taken by data transferred across the web. (Data: Center for Applied Internet Data Analysis)

CHINA: STRICT CENSORSHIP

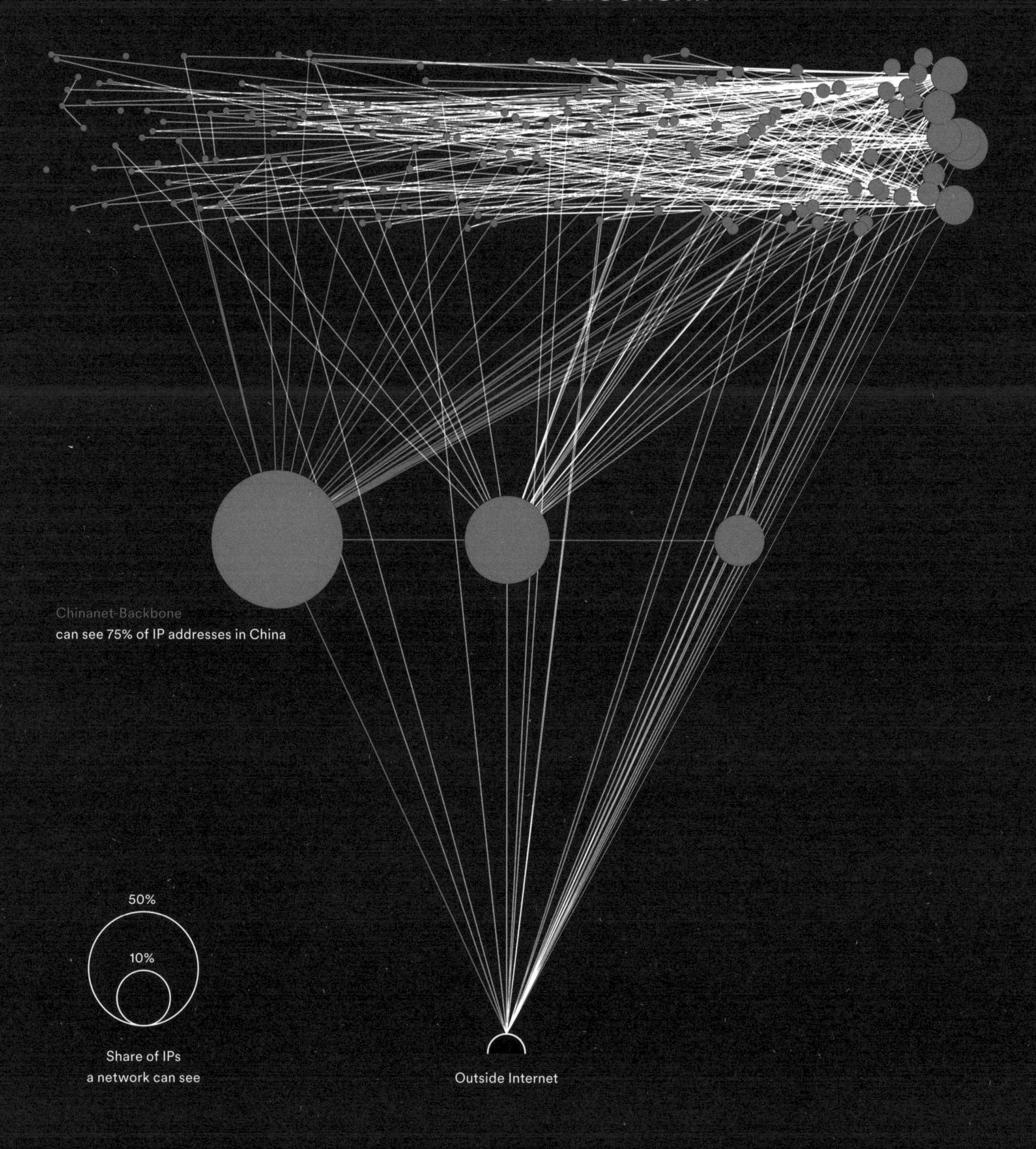

China is notorious for its censorship and surveillance of the internet. Research estimates that nearly 75% of Chinese IP addresses go through AS 4134, Chinanet-Backbone, which is the 15th largest AS in the world in terms of the number of IPs it serves. Chinanet-Backbone is known to be a point at which China performs filtering, preventing certain kinds of information from entering or leaving the country. A 2011 paper from researchers at the University of Michigan found that of all the AS networks in the country, the Chinanet AS, and those of its branch companies across China were responsible for more filtering than any others.

RUSSIA: RADICAL DECENTRALIZATION

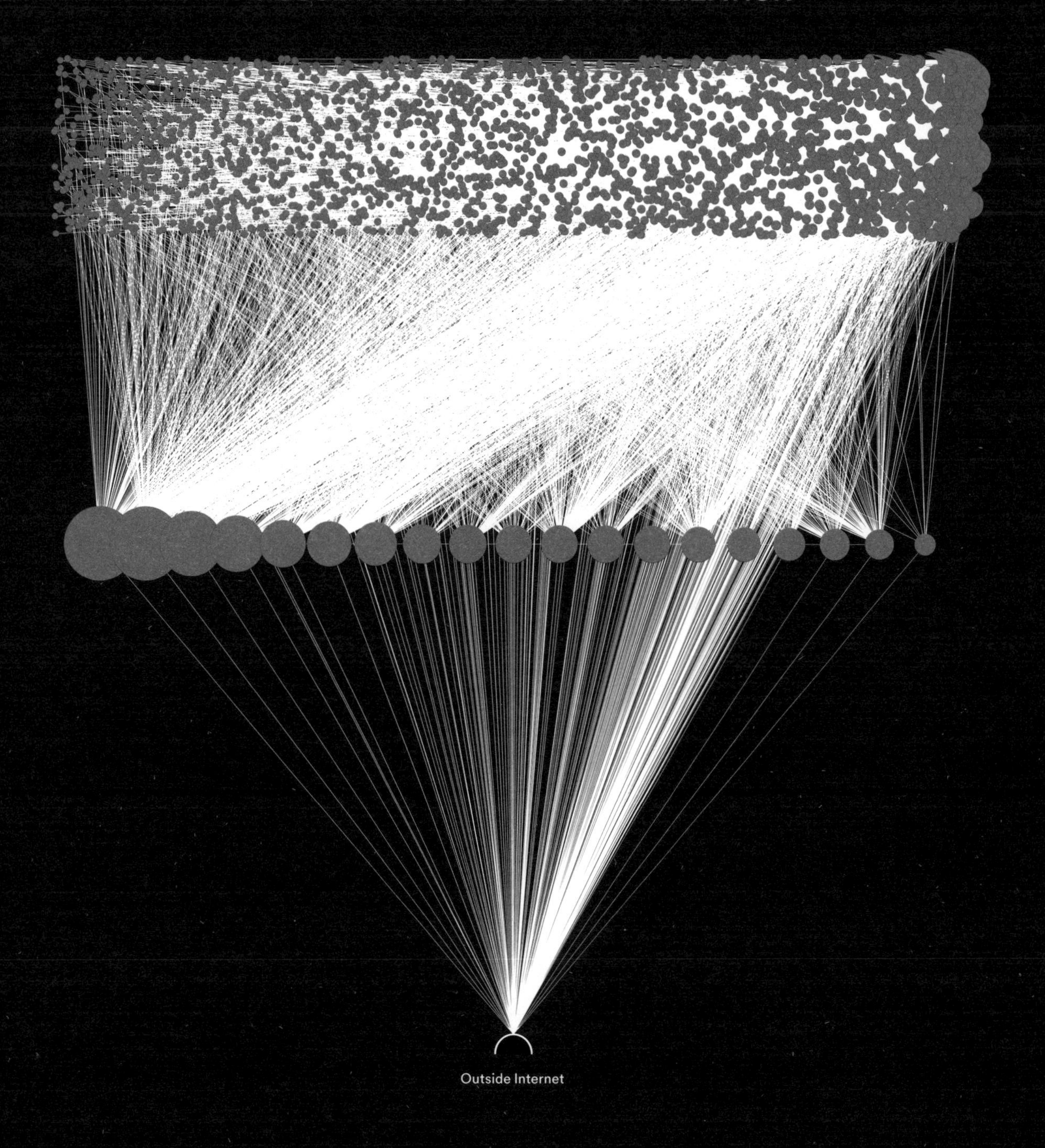

Russia's internet is radically decentralized, which is surprising, given its president's authoritarian tendencies. The best explanation for this is cybercrime. A 2007 study of the Russian Business Network, a massive cybercrime operation based in St. Petersburg, reveals how its creators built "a nebulous network to blur the understanding of their activities." By creating intentionally complex systems, cybercriminals can both hide their tracks and make their systems very difficult to shut down from the outside. The trade-off with such a system is that Russia loses some ability to track and censor its networks. So while Russia may be considered a larger threat to the US than China when it comes to cybercrime, it has been soliciting China for advice on how to restructure its internet at the same time. (Data: Center for Applied Internet Data Analysis)

- **February 2015**

On Feb. 1, an outage in a Fujitsu data center in Perth during a thunderstorm affected the systems of Western Australia's Department of Health. The department cares for the state's population of 2.6 million people and oversees 2.5 million sq km (960,000 sq miles), which is the largest area administered by a single health department in the world. Three months later, Fujitsu announced an AU$10 million (US$7.6 million) update to the data center.

- **September 2015**

On Sept. 20, Amazon Web Services' DynamoDB database service received too many requests from users. AWS had to pause requests, which affected its cloud service. Clients like Netflix, Medium, Pocket, and IMDb experienced slowdowns and disruptions for about five hours.

- **December 2015**

On Dec. 3, a configuration problem in the Microsoft Azure cloud-computing service left users in western and northern Europe without access to their emails for about four hours. The issue caused traffic to be wrongly routed, which in turn caused a service interruption that took down the Office 365 suite.

- **January 2016**

On Jan. 14, a maintenance operation caused a power outage in a Verizon data center, which took down JetBlue's website for about two hours. As a result, 36 JetBlue flights were delayed and four were cancelled.

- **January 2016**

On Jan. 28, GitHub's primary data center experienced a power disruption that caused a quarter of its servers to reboot, which in turn took GitHub's website down for two hours. GitHub's library of open-source code is used by 5.8 million people worldwide.

- **July 2016**

On July 27, three burned-out HVAC fans produced smoke and activated the fire alarm inside a data center in Ottawa, Canada, which forced an evacuation and emergency shutdown. The outage downed email servers and left some 50,000 public-service workers cut off from their emails throughout the day.

- **August 2016**

On Aug. 8, a small fire in a power supply caused a "massive failure" at Delta Airlines' Technology Command Center in Atlanta, which resulted in a loss of power. Some computers were down for five hours and at least 1,900 flights were cancelled over four days. That small fire cost Delta $150 million. (Above: Grounded Delta passengers. Photo by Joe Amon/Denver Post/Getty)

- **February 2017**

On Feb. 28, a typo in code written by an AWS employee resulted in the outage of 54 of the 100 largest online retailers in the world for four hours. Some experienced slowdowns, but Express and Lululemon went offline completely. Risk-analytics startup Cyence estimated a loss of $150 million for S&P 500 companies due to the outage.

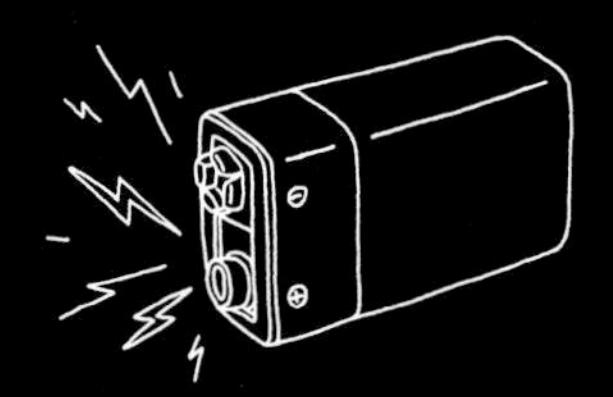

LITHIUM-ION BATTERY

The future of energy

A decade ago, a theory that the world was running out of oil was all the rage. Believers in "peak oil" forecast war, starvation, and general mayhem as nations competed for increasingly scarce fuel. The start of the shale oil boom put an end to that around 2012. Now, a new apocalyptic fever has taken hold: "Peak oil demand" posits that while supply may hold steady for now, it's demand for oil that's running out.

Renewable energy is shouldering its way into the mass market. Solar and wind energy accounted for more than half of the world's new generating capacity in 2016, according to the International Energy Agency. Thanks to new installation techniques and the massive new scale of production, solar energy in particular is becoming as cheap as fossil fuels. In addition, most of the world's big countries are imposing energy-efficiency policies in order to curb fossil-fuel consumption and CO_2 emissions.

But once the sun sets or the wind dies down, renewables falter. Unlike coal, oil, and nuclear energy, the sun and wind can't always deliver electricity whenever it's demanded. To fully switch to renewables, we need to be able to store the energy they generate for use later. In other words, we need better batteries.

Batteries are only now reaching the stage where they can be used in conjunction with renewables. To even begin to match the economics of combustion, they need to be able to store at least four times as much energy as today's best commercial batteries—and to drop in price, too. That could take another decade or more.

↑ Television with batteries and salted popcorn. (Mathery)

THE NEXT GENERATION OF BATTERIES WON'T JUST FUEL OUR CARS—THEY'LL POWER OUR HOMES

Perhaps no single new technology has been as transformational as the lithium-ion battery. In recent decades, transistors have been centrally important, but without the lithium-ion battery, which was invented in 1980, transistors would never have achieved their place in the technological pantheon. There would be no laptop computers as we know them, no iPhones, and no wearable electronics.

For all these achievements, the battery endures plenty of criticism. Why doesn't my phone stay charged longer? Why do headphones explode on transatlantic flights? Why can't electric cars go further and charge faster? And when will I be able to save the electricity produced by my solar panels to use when the sun isn't shining?

Battery makers have a different question: How to snag the hundreds of billions of dollars in annual sales predicted in the next decade?

Lithium-ion has achieved this enviable yet conflicted stature because of its weight. Lithium is the lightest metal on the periodic table, which allows outsized energy to be packed into a tiny space. This makes it the king of batteries.

To be sure, there are problems to be confronted. Cobalt, a primary metal in most lithium-ion batteries, is poisonous, and no one has yet figured out how to neutralize it before disposal; it's also not economical to recycle lithium-ion batteries.

But as the technology evolves, the applications of lithium-ion keep growing, along with the accompanying frenzy. In December 2016, General Motors launched its Chevy Bolt with a driving range of 238 miles (383 kilometers), the most for a mainstream, reasonably priced electric car. And in California, battery makers Tesla, AES, and Altagas have installed gigantic batteries to supplement electric-power grids.

The world these forward-thinking companies foresee is one that uses much less oil for cars and coal in power plants, thus spewing out fewer CO_2 emissions. And, of course, they also imagine thousands of new jobs from the rise of new industries and billions of dollars in new wealth. That's the vision that keeps them going.

↑ Much of the world's lithium used in phones and batteries is harvested from the Uyuni salt flats in Bolivia. (May 2015, Giles Clarke/Getty)

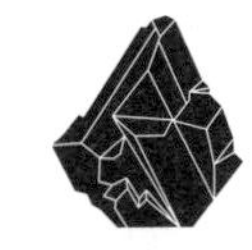

Fear not the lithium cartel

Lithium is mostly produced in a triangle of countries—Argentina, Bolivia, and Chile—and just four companies control 90% of the market: Albemarle and FMC of the US, China's Tianqi, and Chile's SQM. When demand rose in 2015 and 2016, a perceived global shortage of battery-grade lithium caused the element's price in China to triple to more than $20,000 per metric ton.

Although reminiscent of the history of oil monopolies, the current concentration of the lithium market is less troubling than it looks. The market is already reacting to the forecasted surge in lithium's demand by developing new mines. By 2018, the world's lithium shortage is expected to turn into a surplus, with supply climbing by about 70% over the following decade. That should send prices plunging to a quarter of today's levels.

A man sunbathing at a rooftop spa next to solar-cell panels in Berlin, Germany. The popularity of solar energy in Europe's biggest economy has shown that a renewable-power grid doesn't always need a sun-drenched desert or windswept plain to function. (April 30, 2010, Sean Gallup/Getty)

ENERGIEWENDE: GERMANY'S NATIONAL GAMBLE ON GREEN ENERGY

The residents of Schönau, a small town of pitched roofs in Germany's Black Forest, have been on a crusade to power their homes using only renewable energy since the 1980s. They are driven by two nightmares: climate change and nuclear disaster.

Germany's economy was once almost entirely powered by coal and nuclear energy. The former is the most polluting of all fossil fuels. The latter is low-carbon but became deeply unpopular in Germany following the 1986 nuclear disaster in Chernobyl, which exposed thousands of Europeans to radioactive contamination. In its wake, Germany began a decisive pivot toward wind and solar power in a plan called the Energiewende, or "energy transformation."[23] Its course would later be confirmed by another nuclear disaster: Japan's 2011 Fukushima meltdown.

[23]
In 2016, Morocco's Ministry of Islamic Affairs began equipping hundreds of government-owned mosques with solar panels for electricity, LED lights, and solar-thermal water heaters. With the help of German development agency GIZ, it aims to greenify 600 mosques by 2019.

After Chernobyl, Schönau residents began to take control of their area's energy by disconnecting from nuclear sources and connecting to green ones like wind and solar. In 2009, they became an official co-operative, Elektrizitätswerke Schönau, which now has over 4,500 members. "They think [the Energiewende] is the most important project" in Germany, says Sebastian Sladek, one of the co-op's board members.

This pattern is being replicated all over Germany. In 2005, renewables produced a tenth of the nation's power. By 2016, huge infrastructure investment had pushed that up to 30%.

Globally, investment in renewables hit $286 billion in 2015, more than twice as much as went into coal and gas combined. The following year, China, the world's top polluter, became the world's biggest investor in clean technology.[24] By 2030, the International Energy Agency predicts that renewables will be the world's biggest source of power.

[24]
China's infamous urban smog stems in part from widespread coal burning. But Beijing has committed to sourcing at least 20% of power from renewables by 2030. By mid 2017, the country was operating 37 nuclear reactors and building another 20.

As the zeal of Schönau was replicated around the world, the cost of solar panels plummeted between 1975 and 2015 from close to $100 per watt to just under $1. Wind energy saw similar falls. Meanwhile, low coal and oil prices have discouraged investment in those industries.

The strongest sign of change: In 2015, building new renewable infrastructure became cheaper than building new fossil-fuel plants, as R. Andreas Kraemer, a senior fellow at the Institute for Advanced Sustainability Studies, points out. Investing in renewables was once a gamble—one Schönau's residents, and Germany as a whole, were willing to take, even when it was expensive. Now, says Kraemer, the economics support the ethics.

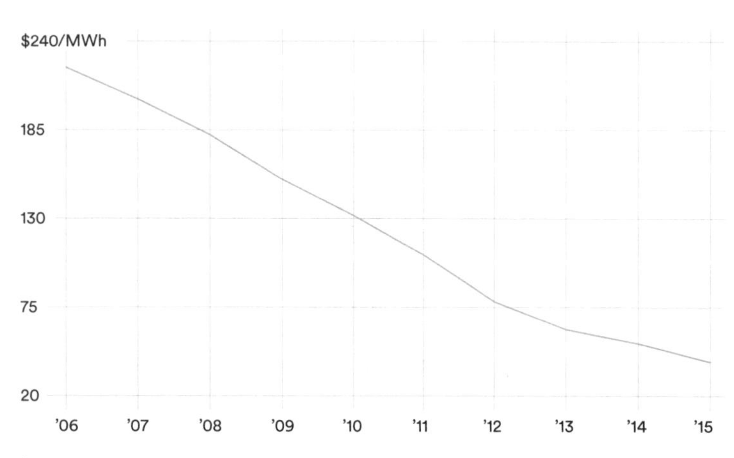

↑ The cost of solar power sold to US utilities, 2006-2015.

NORTH KOREANS HAVE FOUND ENERGY INDEPENDENCE THROUGH CHINESE-MADE SOLAR PANELS

[25]
Noor Ouarzazate Solar Complex is the world's largest concentrated solar plant. Construction began in May 2013 and is expected to be completed in 2018 for a total cost of $9 billion.

[26]
Iceland is the only country that runs on 100% renewable power all the time: 25% from geothermal heat and 75% hydroelectric power.

On the south side of the Yalu River stands a theme park with a ferris wheel and rides that never move. That's about all that catches the eye among the drab, one-story gray buildings of Sinuiju, North Korea from the north side in Dandong, China. China is North Korea's largest trading partner by far. About 70% of that trade flows through Dandong over the Sino-Korean Friendship Bridge. These days, solar panels are in hot demand: Colorful signs on storefronts promise "sun power," [25] and rows of solar panels crowd small shops with brochures promising a higher quality than North Korea's own solar technologies. "North Korean traders are our best clients," says Huo Hong, a local seller. North Korea is mostly powered by outdated coal plants,[26] and although it doesn't lack for coal, residents suffer frequent power outages due to antiquated generators, says John Hopkins University researcher Curtis Melvin. Tired of cold showers and dark rooms, some civilians have found energy independence in renewables. Solar panels dot apartment balconies in the capital, Pyongyang. Made by leading Chinese brands like Haier and Sunrain, the most expensive type of panels sold in Dandong run $400 to $1,000 each (a year's income for many North Koreans), and can power a water boiler. Smaller charging devices for computers and flashlights go for as little as $20. According to the most recent Chinese customs data available, more than 100,000 North Korean households had acquired Chinese-made solar panels by the end of 2014—about 2% of the population. (March 2017. Aurelien Foucault for Quartz)

Bill Gates' reading list on energy

David MacKay's *Sustainable Energy—Without the Hot Air* (2008)

Vaclav Smil's *Energy at the Crossroads: Global Perspectives and Uncertainties* (2003)

Vaclav Smil's *Energies: An Illustrated Guide to the Biosphere and Civilization* (1999)

BILL GATES ON THE BIGGEST BETS IN ENERGY INVESTING

Breakthroughs in energy technologies could reduce air pollution, help people escape poverty, and avoid the worst effects of climate change. But here's the tricky part: We don't yet know which ones will succeed. So we need to explore lots of ideas with investments from both the government and the private sector.

Improved batteries are one possible breakthrough that could help scale existing renewable sources like wind and solar. Solar fuels are another that could power airplanes, trucks, and cargo ships without adding any CO_2 to the atmosphere. These fuels are made by using sunlight to split water into oxygen and hydrogen, then combining the hydrogen with carbon dioxide to make hydrocarbons.

Another path is to make nuclear power safer and cheaper. I founded a business that is working on several approaches to this. The most promising is a traveling wave reactor (TWR) that would run on depleted uranium, a waste product created by today's light-water reactors. A TWR could be sealed up and run for decades without refueling, requiring little maintenance or personnel and reducing the chance of accidents.

A super-efficient power grid is another possible solution. High-voltage direct-current lines—technology already used in China and elsewhere—make it possible to transmit electricity more efficiently over long distances. With a grid like that, the US could generate solar power in Arizona or wind power in the Midwest and transmit it cheaply wherever it's needed.

Figuring out which of these ideas will work, and then deploying them, requires investment from governments and the private sector alike. Government funding gives scientists the freedom to come up with and test bold new ideas, and then private investors take innovation from the lab to the marketplace with companies that deliver solutions at scale.

There is progress on both fronts. In 2015, more than 20 countries and the EU committed to doubling their investments in energy R&D by 2020. And in December 2016, I joined a group of business leaders to launch Breakthrough Energy Ventures, a fund that will invest more than $1 billion in advances that could deliver cheap, reliable, clean energy to the world. The investors involved are patient, understanding that the big breakthroughs may be many years down the road.

This is urgent work. But I am optimistic that, with the right investments, we can make the breakthroughs that will create a clean-energy future for everyone.

Bill Gates

← A composite image released by NASA's Earth Observatory shows the Earth seen from space at night throughout 2016. Clusters of light indicate the use of electricity at night. (Courtesy of NASA)

THE FUTURE OF ENERGY IS UNDER CONSTRUCTION IN AFRICA

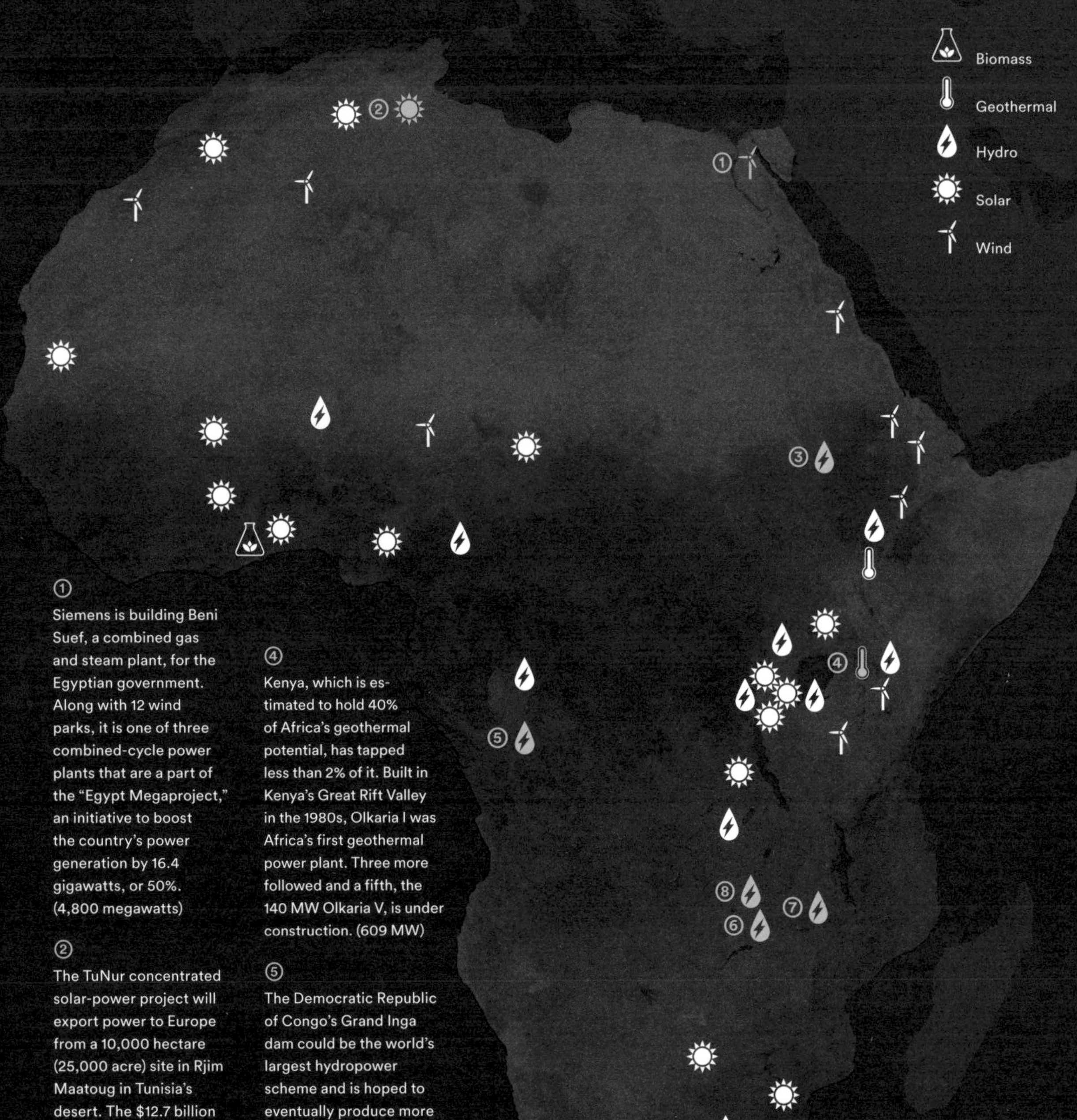

①
Siemens is building Beni Suef, a combined gas and steam plant, for the Egyptian government. Along with 12 wind parks, it is one of three combined-cycle power plants that are a part of the "Egypt Megaproject," an initiative to boost the country's power generation by 16.4 gigawatts, or 50%. (4,800 megawatts)

②
The TuNur concentrated solar-power project will export power to Europe from a 10,000 hectare (25,000 acre) site in Rjim Maatoug in Tunisia's desert. The $12.7 billion project will use a high-voltage direct current to connect to European grids as far away as the UK. (2,500 MW)

③
Ethiopia has a massive hydropower potential of about 45,000 MW. When construction concludes on the Blue Nile's Grand Ethiopian Renaissance dam, its output combined with that of the Gilgel Gibe III dam will almost quadruple the country's electricity capacity. Ethiopia hopes to export the excess. (6,000 MW)

④
Kenya, which is estimated to hold 40% of Africa's geothermal potential, has tapped less than 2% of it. Built in Kenya's Great Rift Valley in the 1980s, Olkaria I was Africa's first geothermal power plant. Three more followed and a fifth, the 140 MW Olkaria V, is under construction. (609 MW)

⑤
The Democratic Republic of Congo's Grand Inga dam could be the world's largest hydropower scheme and is hoped to eventually produce more than a third of Africa's current electricity output. But in July 2016, the World Bank suspended the project's funding due to concerns over how it was being run. (4,800 MW)

⑥
Lake Kariba hydropower station is a shared hydroelectricity station between Zambia and Zimbabwe on the Zambezi river. Constructed between 1956 and 1959, it is the world's largest man-made lake. It is currently being refurbished. (1,830 MW)

⑦
Filled in 1974 and refurbished in 2008, Mozambique's Cahora Bassa dam harnesses the power of the Zambezi River. That energy is sold to neighboring countries, largely South Africa. (2,075 MW)

⑧
Scheduled to finish in 2019, Zambia's Kafue Gorge hydropower station is estimated to cost $2 billion and is one of several hydropower stations in use or under construction in Zambia. (1,400 MW)

⑨
Jeffreys Bay wind farm on the eastern cape is one of the largest of 53 small renewable-energy projects in South Africa. Together, they contribute at least 4,000 MW to the national grid. With more than 40 others underway or planned, the country aims to be generating 13,225 MW by 2025. (138 MW)

TO FREE US ALL FROM FOSSIL FUELS, ELON MUSK HAS BUILT THE NEXT STANDARD OIL

Elon Musk's master plan was simple and, his critics said, doomed. In 2006, the Tesla CEO announced he was going to build a high-end electric sports car, invest the profits in electric vehicles for the masses, and then build the infrastructure to power them all with carbon-free solar electricity.

Ten years later, Musk can almost taste victory. Tesla plans to launch its mass-market Model 3 vehicle in mid 2018, a successor to three luxury models: the Roadster coupe, the Model S sedan, and the Model X SUV. It is building its own battery plant (the Gigafactory) in Nevada, has developed a battery-storage business, and runs at least 200 retail showrooms around the world.[27]

↑ John D. Rockefeller playing golf in 1905. (Time Life Pictures/Mansel/Getty)

What's emerged from this effort is much more than an electric-car company, however: Tesla now has the ability—if not the scale—to supply solar power to run homes and businesses as well as cars.[28] Never shy, Musk said in 2016 that he's on track to build something that has never existed before: "The world's only vertically integrated energy company offering end-to-end clean-energy products to our customers."

Musk is right to insist no single company offers end-to-end renewable energy products. But when you consider energy more broadly, he was beaten to the punch by more than a century.

Standard Oil, the energy giant founded by John D. Rockefeller in 1870, created the playbook for vertical integration in the energy industry. Within three decades of its founding, Standard Oil grew to control more than 90% of refined oil in the US. It ranked among the largest and most profitable companies in history.

In classic vertical integration, companies buy up sources of raw materials, processors, and critical suppliers. Standard Oil did just this, snapping up oil fields and refineries to dominate the oil industry. (It was eventually broken up by the US government in 1911 after the Sherman Antitrust Act brought the era's robber barons to heel.) Today, Musk shares Rockefeller's fanatical strategy to control every aspect of the company's products and the supply chain supporting them.

[27]
In 2016, Japan passed a milestone: Electric-car charging stations became more common than gas stations. (Though some of those charging stations belonged to private individuals.)

[28]
India makes up one fifth of the world's population but uses only 6% of its energy. But the International Energy Agency warns that rapid development means demand is expected to double over the next 25 years, pushing global-warming trends into dangerous territory.

$240.00/MWh
185.00
130.00
75.00
20.00
'06 '07 '08 '09 '10 '11 '12 '13 '14 '15

↑ The cost of wind power sold to US utilities, 2006 to 2015. Data: Berkeley Lab

→ Fire plume after an accident at the Standard Oil refinery in Whiting, Indiana in 1955. (Wallace Kirkland/The LIFE Picture Collection/Getty)

Of course, there are differences. Standard Oil's mission was to monopolize oil; Musk is trying to eliminate it. Rockefeller crushed competitors; Musk gave away Tesla's patents in 2014 to grow the market. Standard Oil was wildly profitable; Tesla has racked up hundreds of millions of dollars in annual losses and has recorded only two profitable quarters since its founding in 2003.

But in many ways, the parallels between the two are clear: Both focused relentlessly on bringing production under one roof. Tesla has made it a mission to make as many of its parts in-house as possible, which is the opposite of the rest of the car industry. Indeed, Musk boasts that Tesla's factories—the "machine that builds the machine"—are the company's future.

"I've refocused most of Tesla engineers into designing the factory," he said in a Febuary 2017 shareholder call. "In the future, the factory will be a more important product than the car itself. Our goal is to be the best manufacturer on Earth."

Economists say the reason for any company to take on such risks is because it can't trust the market to give it what it needs, on the terms it wants. But since the 1990s, companies have run away from this strategy to avoid saddling themselves with liabilities if their business shifted or markets faltered. Cars, for example, are now one of the most distributed products on the planet: American car parts come from more than 4,300 manufacturers spread around the globe. Few car companies own more than a tiny fraction of their supply chain.

Tesla's race in the opposite direction enables it to experiment and rapidly refine its cars—and batteries and solar panels—all while slashing costs. Tesla says manufacturing its own batteries means the price of lithium-ion battery packs are just half of those for other carmakers. To top it off, Tesla is closing deals to buy lithium from mines near its Gigafactory. During a factory tour in 2016, Musk noted with glee that one side of the building could accept raw lithium ore and the other could churn out finished batteries. "It's the most vertically integrated battery factory in the world, and will be more so over time," he said.

Critics point out that Tesla has none of the advantages that were hallmarks of successful vertically integrated companies of the past: healthy profits, deep pockets, and decades of experience managing sprawling enterprises. Skeptical investors have bet billions against it by shorting its stock. But a bet against Musk, at least in recent years, has not been a good one: Tesla's share price soared more than 1,300% between 2010 and 2017, and customers have coughed up an astonishing $373 million in deposits to preorder 373,000 of its $35,000 Model 3 vehicles—a car that doesn't even exist yet.

Of course, Tesla still has to deliver this mass-market car, but Musk isn't sweating it. He wants to do nothing short of creating a solar-electric economy that breaks with the mine-and-burn hydrocarbon economy that has powered the world for hundreds of years. Standard Oil gave Musk a roadmap to do this. But while Rockefeller wanted perfect control of the US oil market in order to sell more oil, Musk will settle for putting an end to it.

Saudi Arabia's plan to quit oil

No one is sure how fast oil will run out. In a decade? Perhaps four decades? Saudi Arabia is not waiting to find out. Reliant on oil exports for 90% of its state budget, the country has launched a plan designed to shift to a mainly non-petroleum economy over the next 20 years. The question is whether the move risks the very instability the ruling royal family is keen to avoid.

Then-deputy crown prince Mohammed bin Salman announced the plan in April 2016. At its core is an IPO for about 5% of the country's crown jewel, Saudi Aramco, the world's biggest oil producer. He will plow the expected $100 billion in proceeds, along with tens of billions more in cash reserves, into a sovereign wealth fund and invest at least half of it in non-oil businesses, especially technology.

But preparing now for an oil-free future carries substantial risks. Prince Mohammed is slashing subsidies, the lubricant that has historically kept the Saudi people on the royal family's side. And the same plan promises to do away with laws that subjugate women, a move that will anger powerful clerics. Yet, the prince's calculus is simple: With only one known factor—the demise of oil—it's better to take risks now to save the kingdom than not to do so, and doom it.

← Inventor and electricity researcher Nikola Tesla in his Colorado Springs laboratory in 1899. (Stefano Bianchetti/Corbis via Getty)

→ Painting by an anonymous North Korean artist depicting a future powered by renewable energy. (Courtesy of Koryo Studio)

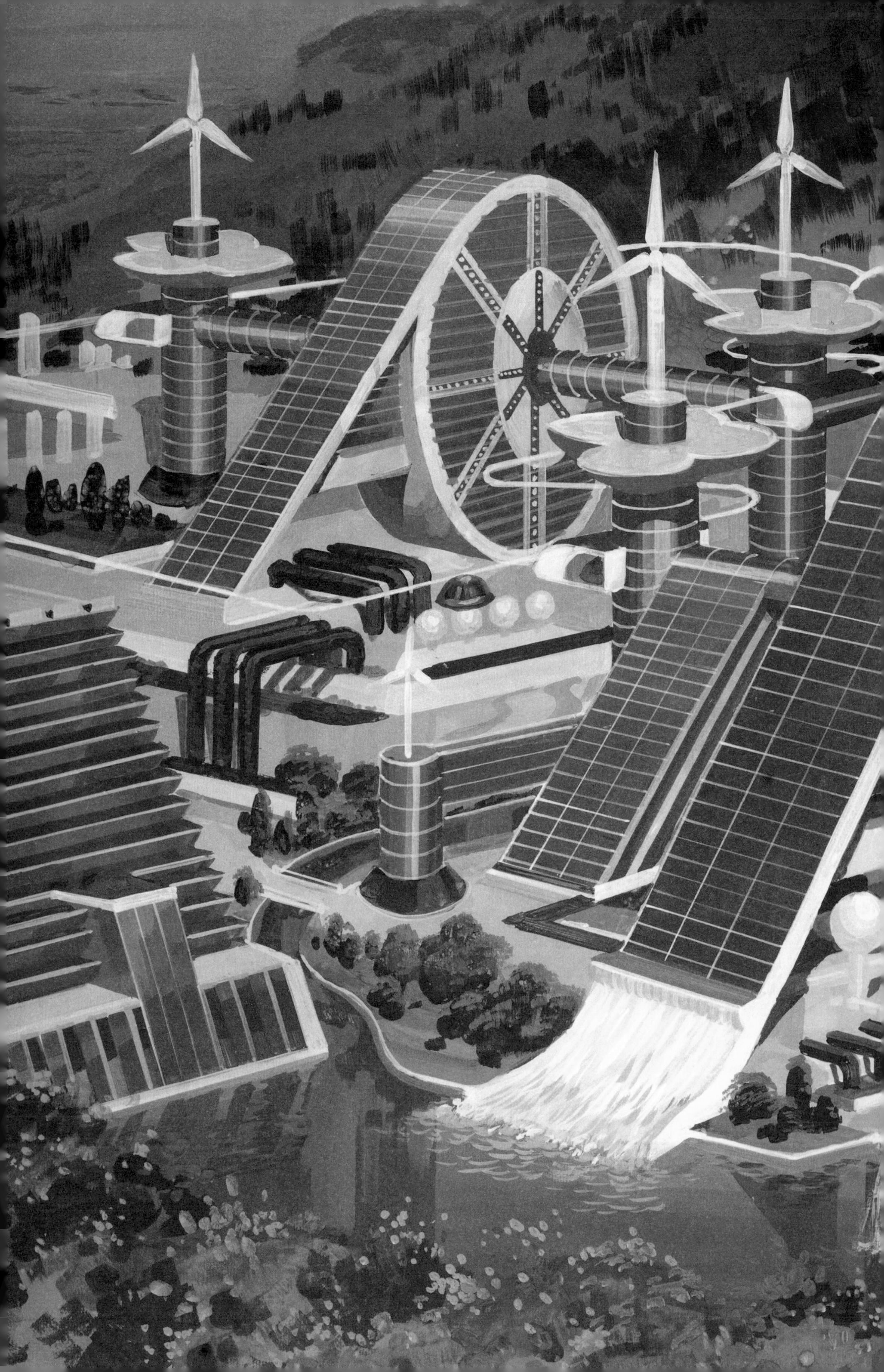

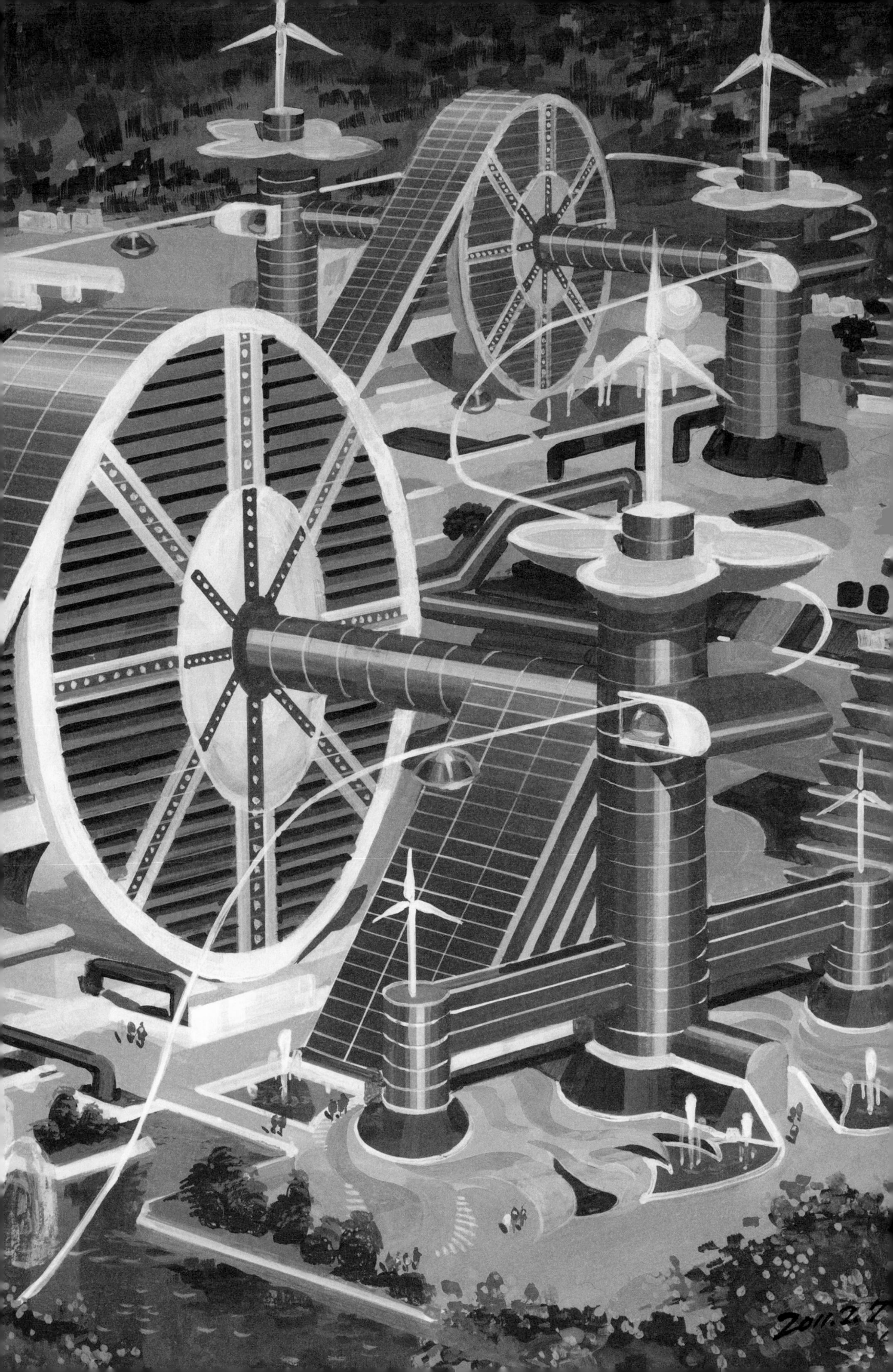
2011.2.7

ALL OF THE CHARTS

Page 4

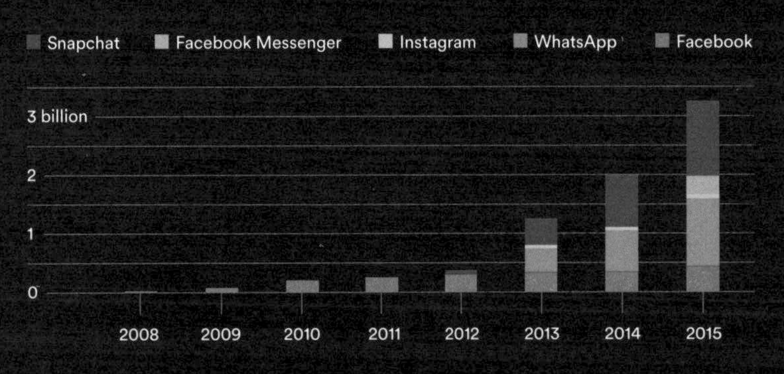

↑ Daily number of photos shared on social-media networks.
Data: Kleiner Perkins Caufield & Byers

Page 26

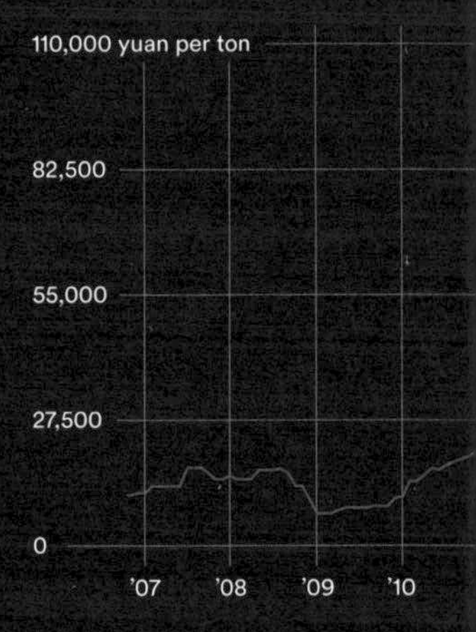

↑ Price of rare-earth carbonate.
Data: Wind Datafeed Service

Page 76

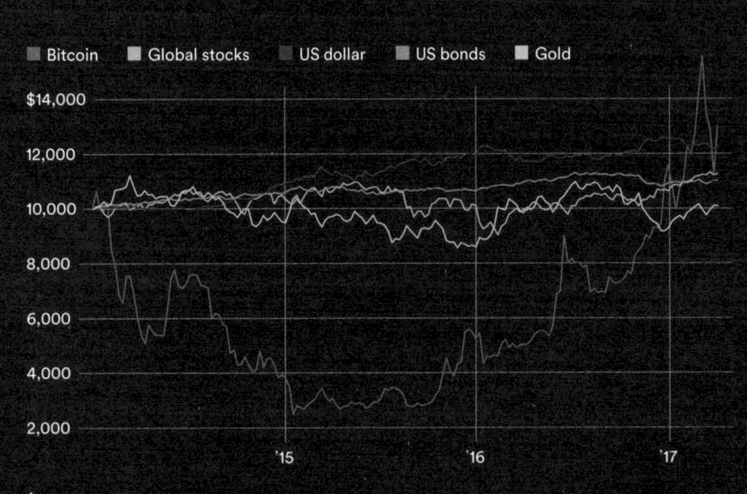

↑ If you had invested in...
Data: Bloomberg, FactSet

Page 77

↑ The value of all bitcoin in circulation
through April 1, 2017. Data: Blockchain.

Page 96

↑ Performance of US-listed data-center REITs, 2012-2016.
Data: FactSet

Page 106

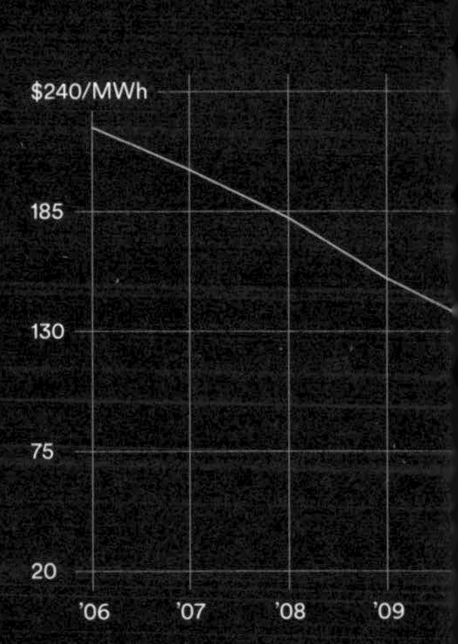

↑ The cost of solar power sold to US util
2006-2015. Data: Berkeley Lab

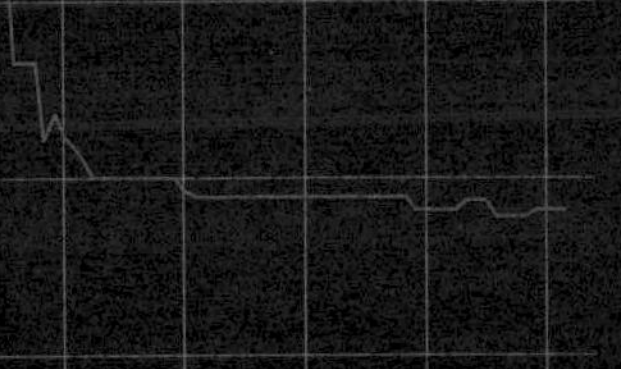

Page 66

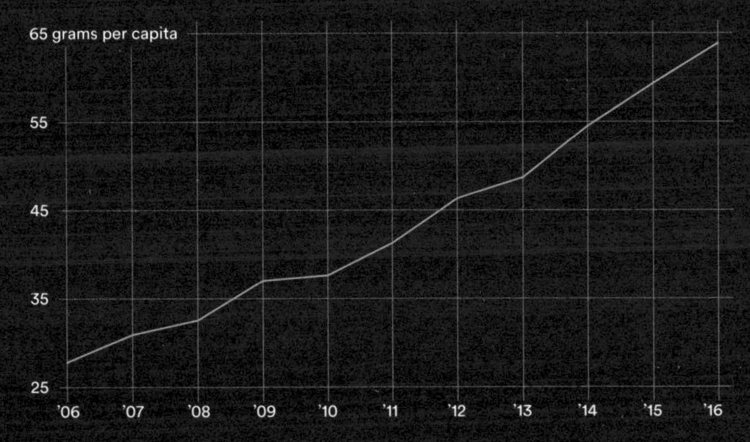

↑ US distribution of amphetamines to treat ADHD.
Data: Automated Reports and Consolidated Ordering System

Page 94

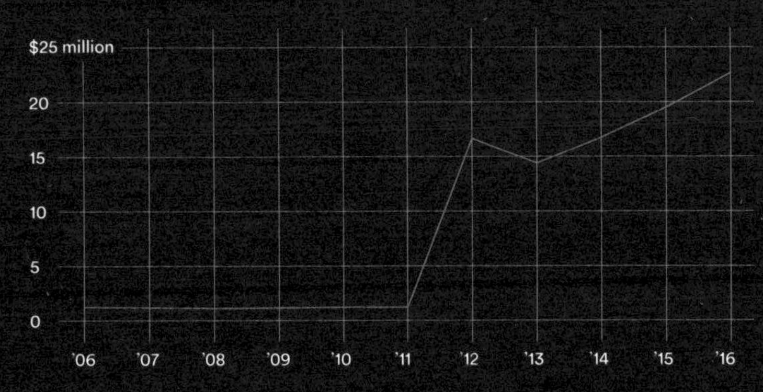

↑ Wage income from information jobs in Crook County, Oregon.
Data: Quarterly Census of Employment and Wages

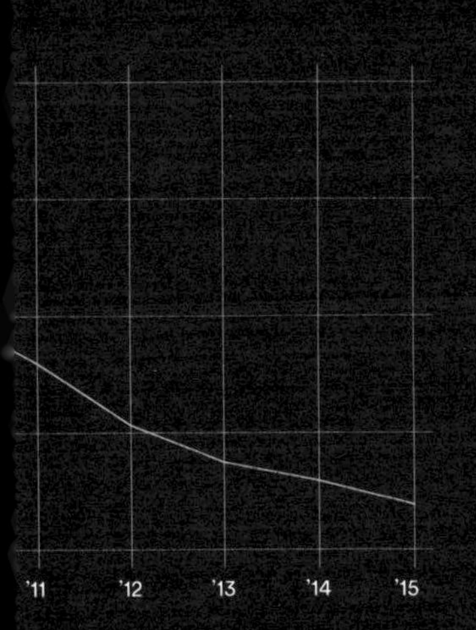

Page 110

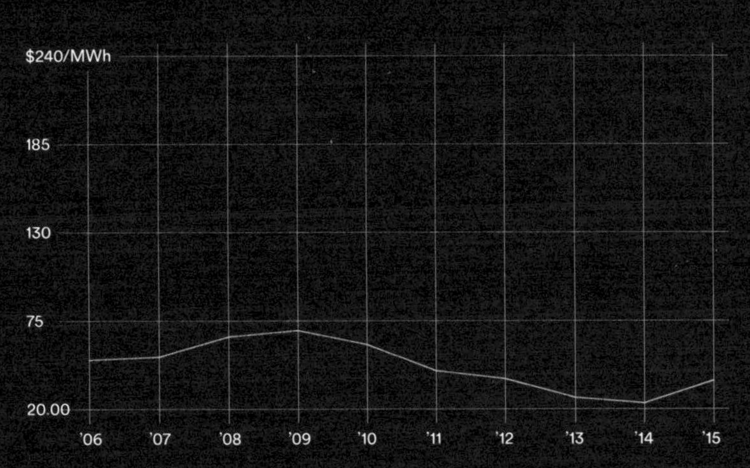

↑ The cost of wind power sold to US utilities, 2006 to 2015.
Data: Berkeley Lab

THIS IS QUARTZ

Quartz was founded in 2012 at a time of enormous change in the global economy. Our mission was to be a guide to those changes for business professionals who care about the entire world, not just what's in front of them. We now reach them through our website, qz.com, as well as emails, apps, and our charting platform, Atlas.

Quartz has offices in New York, London, Hong Kong, San Francisco, and Washington, DC, and journalists everywhere from Johannesburg to São Paulo and Paris. Nearly all of our staff from around the world has contributed to this book in one way or another. Everything else we do is purely digital, so we're excited to be speaking to you for the first time in print.

We would love to see where we are reaching you. If you like, take a photo of the book in your corner of the world and share it on social media with the hashtag #qzobjects, or send it to us privately at qzobjects@qz.com.

Thank you!

→ **Quartz app for iOS and Android**
A news experience that feels like texting with your smart, well-traveled friend.

→ **Atlas**
Tell stories using data with our chart-building tool and sharing platform.

→ **The Daily Brief**
The most important and interesting news from the global economy, delivered to your inbox each morning.

→ **Quartzy, The Newsletter**
Our weekly guide to living with taste, health, and humor, delivered to your inbox just in time for the weekend.

→ **Index**
A new way of highlighting statistics that show how the global economy is changing.

→ **Africa Weekly Brief**
The most important and interesting news from around the continent, delivered to your inbox once a week.

→ **The Quartz Obsession**
Our afternoon email newsletter is a digression into the most fascinating corners of the global economy.

→ **Quartz At Work**
Learn to work better with our new edition, a guide to the changing nature of management and the workplace.

→ **Quartzy, The Edition**
Our guide to the luxuries that make our lives richer—fashion, travel, food, culture, design, entertainment, and most importantly, family, friendships, and wellbeing.

This book is a special project by Quartz.

Concept and editorial direction
Lauren Brown and Caitlin Hu

Creative direction
Ramon Pez

Photo
Johnny Simon

Editing
Xana Antunes, Jason Karaian, Heather Landy, Gideon Lichfield, Matt Quinn, Sarah Slobin, and Elijah Wolfson

Research
Selina Cheng, Lila MacLellan, Luiz Romero, and Molly Rubin

Copy
Georgia Frances King

Facts
Katrina Kaufman

Words
Atossa Abrahamian, Marc Bain, Manu Balachandran, Jackie Bischof, Loretta Chao, Selina Cheng, Joanna Chiu, Lynsey Chutel, Michael Coren, Abdi Latif Dahir, Tim Fernholz, Katherine Foley, Bill Gates, Dave Gershgorn, Devjyot Ghoshal, Gwynn Guilford, Josh Horwitz, Jason Karaian, Madhura Karnik, Yomi Kazeem, Dan Kopf, Lily Kuo, Aislinn Laing, Steve LeVine, Lila MacLellan, Corinne Purtill, Anne Quito, Akshat Rathi, Luiz Romero, Molly Rubin, Allison Schrager, Cassie Werber, Joon Ian Wong, and Elijah Wolfson

Data visualization
Ana Becker, Keith Collins, Martin Krzywinski, Sarah Slobin, Nikhil Sonnad and David Yanofsky

Art
Ana Becker, Fanqiao Wang, AnNam Young

Sales
Joy Robins and Kate Smyres

Marketing
Christopher Chappel, Brian Dell, Cameron Hough, Colette Keane, Zazie Lucke, Mia Mabanta, Alexa Trearchis, and Charlotte White

Communications
Ana Livia Coelho, Emily Lenzner and Sona Rai

Thanks to Zach Seward, Kevin Delaney, and Jay Lauf for creating the universe in which this was possible.

Also thanks to Mathery for letting us play with dry ice and wigs; Adriana Crespo for sending us a pack of gum from Ecuador; Marc Levinson for assisting with research on container standardization; Ken Shirriff for his help on the math for the bitcoin-mining worksheet; the University of the Witwatersrand Historical Papers Research Archive for sharing decades-old mining training manuals; Pietro Renzi for the use of his passport; and to Qualcomm for supporting Quartz's first print product

Additional thanks to Cosimo Bizzarri, Alison Brown, Nicolas Christin, Noreen Dillane, Dusty, Rob Garrigan, Giulia Iacolutti, Jason Maier, Cristian Malisan, Zoe McDougall, Pamela Pez, Jayant Sabnis, Paolo Sidoti, Aleta Stephen, and Greg Wyler

Typefaces
LL Circular, Larish Alte, Univers, Lyon Text

Paper
Salzer Touch, Magno Volume, Cyclus offset

Printed in Italy by Grafiche dell'Artiere

ISBN 978-0-692-90194-6

10 9 8 7 6 5 4 3 2

↑ Composite panorama of the Milky Way seen from Earth, released Sept. 2009.
(European Southern Observatory / Serge Brunier)